VIETNAM

Student Field Manual

Underground Reality: Vietnam Student Manual
Written by: Carey Huffman
Developed by: HigherLife Development Services Inc.
Graphic Design: Principle Creative, Inc
Published by: Living Sacrifice Book Company
P.O. Box 2273
Bartlesville, OK 74005-2273
www.undergroundreality.com

ISBN 978-1-936034-13-0

Contents

Check out "Look to Love"
at undergroundreality.com

Message from SonicFlood

We were blown away when we heard about what The Voice of the Martyrs does for Christians who are persecuted around the world. So when VOM invited us to host the video sessions for *Underground Reality: Vietnam*, we were totally on board.

Every week Rick Heil and Spencer Dalton will introduce the video session and at the end they will talk honestly about how it impacted them. Their world was rocked by the video sessions, and yours will be, too.

This experience inspired us to write a new song about going deeper with God titled "Look to Love." You'll get a chance to listen to this song during your sessions together, and we pray the lyrics will open your eyes to how God can use you.

God is going to touch your heart as you take the journey with these eight teenagers into a communist country where religion is considered a threat to the powers of the state. You will find your own faith set on fire, and you are going to be filled with desire to grow deeper in your faith and support your brothers and sisters in Christ around the world.

SonicFlood

Rick Heil (vocals)
Ben Davis (bass)
Spencer Dalton (drums)
Preston Dalton (guitars)
McKendree Tucker (keyboards)

What Is It Costing You to Follow Christ?

You're about to embark on an adventure that will change your life forever. That's what happened to the eight teens with whom you'll share this experience. Over the next nine weeks you'll relive a mission to smuggle Bibles into communist-controlled Vietnam. Your journey to visit the underground church will open your eyes to the hardships faced by countless Christians around the world. In the process, you'll gain appreciation for the opportunities you have to worship and serve God freely.

Course Goals

To help you develop an active awareness and appreciation for the persecuted church worldwide.

To challenge you toward a radically devoted, completely surrendered, all-out pursuit of Jesus Christ and His purposes for your life—regardless of the cost.

At this moment, in many parts of the world, people are harassed, mistreated, and denied basic human rights for identifying with Jesus. Many are imprisoned. Some are tortured or even killed. This is nothing new. It has happened throughout history to those who boldly follow Christ in a world that persistently defies God and persecutes His people. In this study, you'll encounter the stories of many faithful people who have willingly sacrificed all to serve Christ.

Dear friends, do not be surprised at the painful trial you are suffering, as though something strange were happening to you. But rejoice that you participate in the sufferings of Christ, so that you may be overjoyed when his glory is revealed. If you are insulted because of the name of Christ, you are blessed, for the Spirit of glory and of God rests on you (1 Peter 4:12–14).

FAMILY IMPACT

Wow! The tone and passion from the blogs... was really intense! I got chills just reading some of them. It sounds like God saved the best for last...The passion, courage, and joy that the Vietnamese display in their service to God is very sobering, especially in the midst of so much active persecution. They appear to have so little in the earthly realm but are clinging daily to what really matters in the scope of eternity...Our prosperity, comfort, and myriad options to deal with in most any situation that confronts us in the rich Western countries certainly form a barrier to exercising faith that builds our trust in God. I believe we have much more to learn from the persecuted church than they have to learn from us.

Bryant's Dad

A Story of Extreme Sacrifice

In an effort to influence Romanian citizens, the communist regime recruited four thousand ministers to attend a special congress to publicly proclaim support for the new government. As one pastor after another made cowardly speeches asserting the partnership of Christianity and communism, Sabina Wurmbrand whispered to her husband, "Richard, stand up and wash away this shame from Jesus' face." Richard responded, "If I speak, you will lose your husband." But Sabina replied, "I don't wish to have a coward for a husband." So when Richard took the stand he defiantly pronounced, "It's not our duty to praise earthly powers...but to glorify God the Creator and Christ the Savior."

From then on, Richard was a marked man. In February of 1948 he was kidnapped and thrown into prison where he endured years of solitary confinement, beatings, and attempted brainwashing. Richard faithfully endured two prison terms for a total of fourteen years. Sabina was also arrested and forced to labor on the Danube Canal. In 1964, Richard and his family were ransomed out of Romania for $10,000. They came to the U.S. and started a ministry known as Jesus to the Communist World (later changed to The Voice of the Martyrs, or VOM). In the course of his travels, Richard aimed to educate the free world about the atrocities committed against Christians in communist countries and other restricted nations.

For more than forty years, VOM has raised awareness of and brought help to the persecuted church. This is the organization that sent the Underground Reality team into Vietnam and produced the resources for this study. For further background and information on The Voice of the Martyrs and the persecuted church worldwide, go to www.persecution.com.

Richard Wurmbrand

"Doing the work of God is dangerous—not doing it is more dangerous."

—Sabina Wurmbrand
(VOM co-founder)

Introduction from The Voice of the Martyrs

Dear Teen,

An amazing number of Christians we meet in restricted nations—many of whom have suffered greatly for their faith in Christ—are young. I often think of a young man nicknamed "Pencil," who planted a church in a political prisoner camp in North Korea—and gave his life there—before his twentieth birthday. His is one story among countless others.

Most Christians in the West do not suffer for their faith in the same way that some brothers and sisters are suffering. But all Christians are called to *remember* their suffering (Hebrews 13:3) and to *fellowship* with them (Philippians 3:10). These are the two reasons The Voice of the Martyrs sent eight teenagers to Vietnam to meet with persecuted Christians—to remember and to fellowship. Each teen came back from the trip changed and challenged.

Now if we are children, then we are heirs—heirs of God and co-heirs with Christ, if indeed we share in his sufferings in order that we may also share in his glory. I consider that our present sufferings are not worth comparing with the glory that will be revealed in us (Romans 8:17–18).

We didn't want that transformation to end with eight people. We filmed their trip, and now we are sharing it with you. You will feel some intense emotions as you journey with them through Vietnam, a communist country where the government sees Christianity as a threat to its authority. At the same time, you will learn truths from your persecuted brothers and sisters that will sustain you in your own trials.

God has a specific plan to impact the kingdom through you. Our prayer is that *Underground Reality: Vietnam* will increase your faith and inspire you to do all you can for Him.

For those in bonds,

Tom White

Tom White
Executive Director, VOM

For More Info...

www.undergroundreality.com. At this exciting, teen-oriented website, you can read more Underground Reality Blogs and Reality Blog Archives. While you're there you can review the video sessions. The site also contains news, discussion groups, and other resources.

www.persecution.com. This website has the latest news regarding the persecuted church around the world. You'll also find country information, news releases, video clips, and ways to pray for and help persecuted Christians around the world.

God Is Calling You

Session #1

WHAT's the Point?

Jesus calls us to follow Him with complete and total sacrifice.

WHY Does It Matter?

Only when we abandon our own way and surrender totally to Christ can we fulfill God's ultimate purpose for our lives.

HOW Can I Live It?

Entrust your life to Jesus and put aside anything that could keep you from following Him and fulfilling His purposes.

Bible Basis

As Jesus was walking beside the Sea of Galilee, he saw two brothers, Simon called Peter and his brother Andrew. They were casting a net into the lake, for they were fishermen. "Come, follow me," Jesus said, "and I will make you fishers of men." At once they left their nets and followed him. Going on from there, he saw two other brothers, James son of Zebedee and his brother John. They were in a boat with their father Zebedee, preparing their nets. Jesus called them, and immediately they left the boat and their father and followed him (Matthew 4:18–22).

(If you missed this week's session, go to www.undergroundreality.com to watch part 1 of Session 1, "God Is Calling You").

"It remains for the world to see what the Lord can do with a man wholly consecrated to Christ."
—Henry Varley (1835–1912)

The Challenge

Are you ready to step out of your comfort zone, walk away from life-as-usual, venture into the unknown, and take the extreme plunge into a lifestyle of total surrender to Christ? That's how Jesus' first and most devoted disciples pursued life with Him. And this is the challenge Jesus has always set before His followers to this day: "If anyone would come after me, he must deny himself and take up his cross and follow me. For whoever wants to save his life will lose it, but whoever loses his life for me and for the gospel will save it" (Mark 8:34–36). How will you respond to the call?

As you consider your answer, keep in mind that choosing to follow Christ doesn't mean that you'll always be certain about what's ahead. You can, however, be certain of this: Despite your perceived limitations and insecurities, Jesus invites you to trust Him. If you accept this invitation, He will enable you to follow His call, no matter where it leads or what His purposes involve.

Consider this week's key text, Matthew 4:18–22. When Jesus called His first disciples, notice how they immediately left their families and jobs to follow Him. Think about this for a moment. They put everything else aside and immediately made Jesus top priority in their lives. Christ asks the same of us today, calling us from life as we know it to a life of complete abandonment and total sacrifice for the sake of the gospel. **Why do you think the disciples willingly left all that was familiar to them to follow Jesus? What did He offer that was so compelling?**

As you follow Jesus and reach out to others with His love, you'll often face opposition from the very people you are attempting to reach. And yet Jesus still commands us to demonstrate His character and deliver His message—even when it's extremely inconvenient. **Over the next several weeks, you'll be challenged—perhaps like never before—to follow Jesus anywhere and to deepen your devotion to Him, regardless of the cost. At this moment in other parts of the world, there are countless Christians who are harassed and mistreated simply for associating with Jesus. Some are imprisoned. Some are tortured or even killed. Why is this happening?**

Read John 15:18–21 and 16:33. Shortly before Jesus left the earth and returned to heaven, He warned His followers that they would face hatred and opposition—just as He had—in the world. What does it mean that the world will hate Jesus' followers, and why is this so? What comes to mind when you hear the word *persecution*? In what ways might Christians experience it?

Read Matthew 8:18–22 and Mark 10:17–31. If you weren't careful, what could take priority over God in your life or what could hold you back from following His purposes?

How can you ensure that this doesn't happen?

Read Matthew 28:19–20 and Acts 1:8. What assurance does Jesus give us as we continue to fulfill His final commission?

Live, from Vietnam

Most people—particularly younger people—learn best through relationships and shared experiences. Over the next nine weeks, you have the opportunity to relive the adventures of eight teens on a mission to smuggle Bibles into communist-controlled Vietnam. Your journey with them into the "underground church" will open your eyes to the hardships faced by countless Christians around the world. As your awareness of the persecuted church increases, you'll gain a greater appreciation for the freedoms and opportunities you have to worship and serve God. In the process, you'll be challenged toward a radically-devoted, completely surrendered, uncompromising, all-out pursuit of Jesus Christ and His purposes for your life.

Visit www.undergroundreality.com to see and hear more from the mission team regarding their adventures in Vietnam. While you're there, review the first part of Session 1, "God Is Calling You." **Which teen from the video do you most identify with and why?**

DID YOU KNOW?

There are over 60 known languages in Vietnam, including many tribal languages. Yet it is illegal for most people there to have Bibles in their own language.

The Underground Reality: Vietnam Mission Team

Meet the Team

- Brad is the designated worship leader.
- Wes is in charge of the "teen" cam.
- Bethany refers to herself as the "Vietnamese Santa Claus."
- Bryant and Tanni are the team journalists.
- Shannon and Jon are the team photographers.
- Daniel (D.J.) helps on special presentations for various settings.

FRONTLINE DIARIES

Arriving in Saigon

We arrived late this morning in Saigon (Ho Chi Minh City)... It was very hot, humid, and rainy... We are also being reminded of a key word working in Vietnam—flexibility. Over half of the initial plans have changed for one reason or another, and we are scrambling to reschedule events...

At the hotel, the teens met up with Summer and Lihn. They are daughters of a pastor who has been in prison too many times to count...

It went very well, and the teens had a chance to ask questions. DJ wanted to know why Christians didn't just fight back. Yes, this is the same DJ who was a bit terrified by the kids armed with chewing gum! :)

Bethany got to attend an unregistered house church meeting tonight. She just came back while I was typing and was VERY excited about the service.

Steve

(one of the leaders/producers of UR:Vietnam)

Visit www.undergroundreality.com to read more from the Underground Reality Blogs and Reality Blog Archives. The site also provides direction in praying for persecuted Christians in Vietnam and around the world.

Persecution Around the World

Algeria has suffered from civil war for nearly half a century, and tens of thousands have perished. Algeria is 97% Muslim, and a new law restricting Christian evangelism was implemented in March 2006. Conversion to Christianity is a crime punishable by death There are almost no church buildings, and only two of the 50 spoken languages have a New Testament translation. While Christians say that public persecution by the government has nearly disappeared with the fall of the Taliban, they are still not free to practice their faith openly without harsh resistance from radical Muslims.

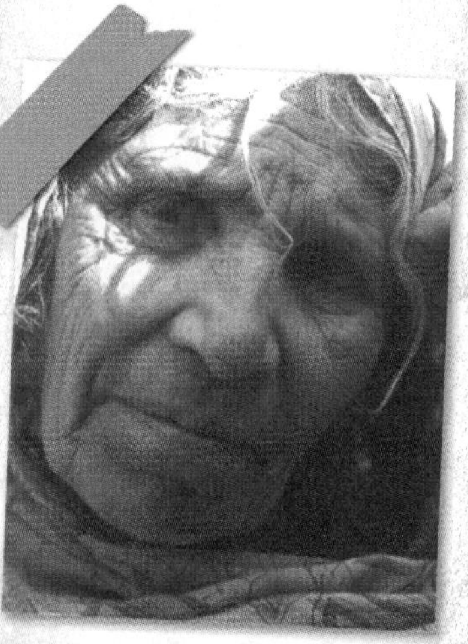

Visit www.persecution.com for the latest news from the persecuted church around the world.

You'll also find country information, news releases, video clips, and ways you can directly bless persecuted Christians.

Real-Time Response

How do you think you would feel about the prospect of going on a ministry trip to a country like Vietnam that severely restricts Christianity?

Do Christians today, in this country, experience persecution? How so?

Do you ever feel bored—like you're in a spiritual rut? How so and why?

Real-Time Response, continued

What do you think it would take to shake things up in your spiritual life, inspiring you toward a deeper faith and relationship with Jesus?

How do you think this compares to what believers experience in other parts of the world?

The Persecuted Church

The government in Indonesia forces people to carry an identification card that includes their religious status. Militant Muslims have killed more than 8,000 Christians and destroyed more than 700 churches since 1996.

In Perspective

List things that you may need to put aside or put in perspective in order to follow Jesus completely. These include things that could distract you from God's plan for your life.

1

2

3

4

5

6

7

God may or may not ask you to give up certain things. But He definitely won't tolerate anything taking priority over Him. Pray for God's help in keeping all things in proper perspective and allowing nothing to come between you and Him.

Real-Time Response, continued

Why is it often difficult to surrender completely to Christ? What do you think God could accomplish through you if you totally sold out to His purposes?

How will you respond to God's call on your life?

Just like Perpetua in Roman times, this young girl has faced persecution from the Vietnamese government.

Bold Believers

Conversion to Christianity was against Roman law in A.D. 202 when a young wealthy mother named Perpetua was arrested for her newfound faith. Perpetua's father begged her to consider her baby and renounce her beliefs. But Perpetua refused to put love for family ahead of Christ. Along with her servant girl Felicitas, she remained imprisoned until March 7, 203, when the two women were thrown into the arena to be mauled by wild animals. Perpetua was tossed by a wild heifer, but when she noticed Felicitas was injured, she got up and went to her. As the two women leaned on one another, the beasts refused to attack. So gladiators entered the arena to finish the execution. But the man assigned to Perpetua was young and inexperienced. His hand trembled as he tried to pierce between her ribs. Perpertua cried out as the sword struck her to the bone, but then she calmly took the man's hand and guided the sword to her throat. One observer said, "It was as though so great a woman could not be killed unless she herself were willing."

Perpetua responded to Jesus' call, literally abandoning all else to follow Him. Her bold decision cost her everything in this life. But she willingly traded it all for the honor and reward of identifying with her Savior. Is this a price you are willing to pay? Perhaps you doubt that you could endure such intense persecution. But if you will respond to God's call and simply follow where Jesus leads, He will give you the strength to stand for Him, no matter what.

Look at the lyrics from SonicFlood's song, "Look to Love."

Life's too short
For you to close your eyes
Let love be your guide
Take my hand
Step into the light
Let love be our guide

If we all live for something
Then we won't die for nothing
Lift your head and look to love
Pray for hope that overcomes
Broken hearts with empty dreams
That only God can make complete

Life's a road
Filled with empty souls
Let love make you whole
If we just take the chance to love
Leaving our selfishness to rust
Then we could be the light that's
leading their way home

Look to love
Live to love
Cry for love
Die for love

Today, I Pray

Write a simple prayer, asking God for the strength and desire to answer His call and "be the light" that leads someone else home.

Religion in Vietnam

- Buddhist 54%
- Christian 8%
- Cao Dai/Hoa Hoa 6%
- Muslim 0.7%
- non-Religious 22%
- Traditional ethnic 8%
- Chinese 1%
- Baha'i 0.4%

Constitutional guarantees of religious freedom are meaningless, as government policy controls all religious activity, including Buddhism.

The Word Thru-the-Week

READ: Luke 5:27–28

THINK: Do you respond to Jesus without hesitation?

PRAY: Pray for passion in pursuing Christ without reservation.

READ: 1 Peter 4:12–13

THINK: How do you handle the hardships that God's Word says will come?

PRAY: Ask Jesus for strength in the face of opposition and thank Him for the ultimate victory.

READ: Mark 10:17–31

THINK: Is anything holding you back from fulfilling God's perfect plan for your life?

PRAY: Ask God to keep you fully dependent on Him.

READ: Matthew 8:18–22

THINK: What comforts are you willing to put aside for Jesus?

PRAY: Ask God to show you the joy of sacrifice in following Jesus.

READ: 2 Peter 1:3–11

THINK: In what areas do you need to exercise greater discipline and self-control? How do you engage the world with the gospel yet remain uncorrupted by it?

PRAY: Ask God to keep you from being corrupted by the world and to help you grow consistently in your relationship with Him.

READ: Matthew 28:19–20; Acts 1:8

THINK: What does Jesus call His followers to do and how can you respond to that call from where you are right now?

PRAY: Give thanks to Jesus for enabling you to follow Him and accomplish His purposes through the power of the Holy Spirit.

Remember to go to www.undergroundreality.com and www.persecution.com for direction and inspiration regarding how to pray daily for persecuted Christians around the world.

I Dare You

This week's mission, should you choose to accept it: Put aside anything that could hinder you from following Christ and fulfilling God's purposes for your life with total devotion. Refer to the "In Perspective" list you made a few pages back. Without hesitation, take action to quit, give up, or get rid of anything that allows ungodly images or influences to affect your thoughts or behavior. Realign your priorities if anything is taking precedence over devotion and service to God. Rely on God's help and strength in making these changes. Be sure to replace these things with godly activities, behaviors, and pursuits.

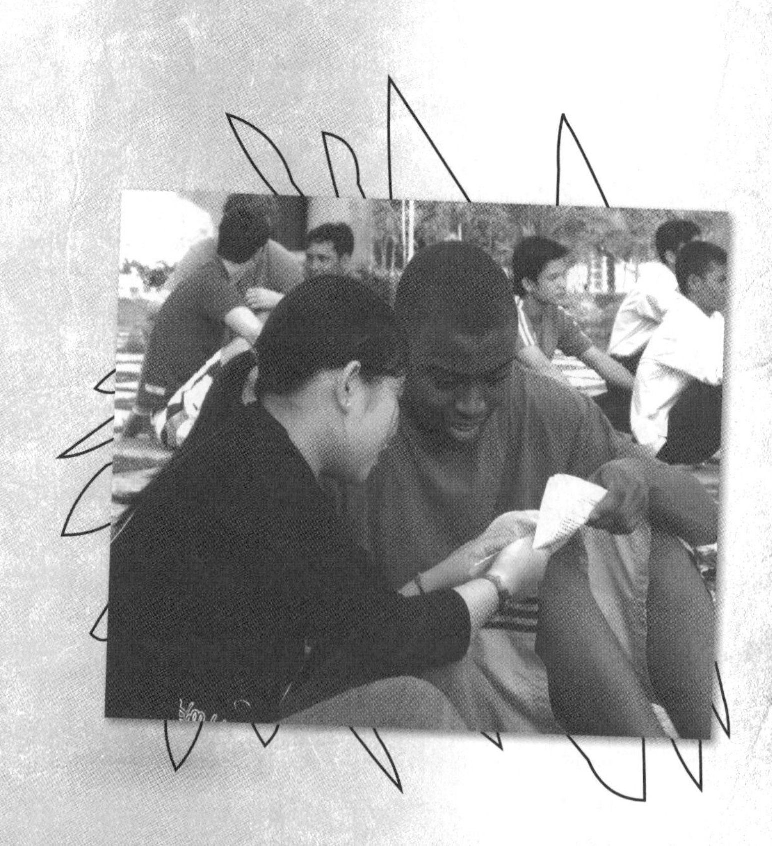

*My Priorities

1 ____________________

2 ____________________

3 ____________________

4 ____________________

5 ____________________

6 ____________________

7 ____________________

8 ____________________

9 ____________________

10 ____________________

Make a list of what your priorities are today. Refer to this list often as you go through the rest of the sessions. Write down any changes you see in your priorities.

Session #2

Trust in the Trenches

Why does God allow things to happen that seem to hinder us from fulfilling His purpose?

WHAT's the Point?

By allowing us to experience difficulty and uncertainty, God teaches us to rely on Him for strength, guidance, and fulfillment.

WHY Does It Matter?

If serving God was always easy, we would fail to depend fully on Him and would be unlikely to grow spiritually.

HOW Can I Live It?

Trust God completely at all times and depend on Him to guide and strengthen you through difficult circumstances.

Bible Basis

Trust in the LORD with all your heart and lean not on your own understanding; in all your ways acknowledge him, and he will make your paths straight (Proverbs 3:5–6).

"God is ready to assume full responsibility for the life wholly yielded to Him."
—Andrew Murray (1828–1917)

The Challenge

(If you missed this week's session, go to www.undergroundreality.com to watch Session 2, "Trust in the Trenches.")

Last week you considered how Jesus called you to follow Him and to fulfill a mission. But what happens when suddenly you encounter roadblocks? They may be physical, emotional, relational, financial, or spiritual. They can involve difficult circumstances, opposition from people, or issues in your own mind. Regardless of the setback, God invites you to trust Him, rather than relying on yourself. This is particularly challenging when life doesn't seem fair. But consider the countless people around the world who are unjustly denied the liberties we enjoy to openly express ourselves, including the freedom to gather for ministry and worship. Christians in Vietnam and other restricted countries deal with persistent threats from authorities and are constantly persecuted. They must trust God for everything. We can learn a lot from their faith and experience.

Consider this week's key text, Proverbs 3:5–6. Why is it sometimes difficult to trust God?

It can be particularly troubling to encounter extreme difficulties when trying our best to do what God desires. **Why do we often encounter roadblocks when trying to do God's will, and why does God allow things to happen that seem to get in the way of us fulfilling His purposes?**

What do you think it means to trust in the Lord with "all your heart" and to acknowledge Him in all your ways? Why must you do this first—before you expect God to provide an answer or direct your path?

True dependence on God means trusting Him even when you don't have answers or see a clear path. Difficulty and uncertainty test our faith in God. **Does complete trust in God mean that you don't take responsibility or some sort of action in the situation yourself? Why or why not? What's the balance between trusting God and doing what you can to make the best of a situation?**

Read Matthew 12:38 and John 20:29. Many people want a sign from God before they'll trust in Him. But God blesses those who rely on Him even when they don't sense His presence or see the affects of their faith. **Describe a situation or aspect of life in which you've had difficulty trusting God, and why. What have you learned from the experience?**

Read Acts 17:26–27. Why do you think God has you in the particular place you are right now?

God created you with purpose and destiny, and He gives you the opportunity to trust Him. He didn't put you right here, right now just so you could do your own thing. Rather, He's given you the responsibility and privilege of reaching people who don't know Christ and helping others who are persecuted for following Him. **Read 1 Peter 2:11–12. What does it means to live "as aliens and strangers in the world, to abstain from sinful desires, which war against your soul"?**

How can you live so that others can't deny the good you do because of your faith in Christ?

"The tragedy of life is not that it ends so soon, but that we wait so long to begin it."
—Richard Evans (1906–1971)

Live, from Vietnam

Last week you met eight teens headed for Vietnam to smuggle Bibles to Christians there. This week you witnessed their first contact with Vietnamese nationals. This brought out a range of conflicting emotions among team members, as they reflected on the history of Vietnam and how their perspectives and freedoms compared with their Vietnamese hosts. The missions team also had their first encounter with the underground church—believers who must worship God in secret—as they participated in an evening youth service outside of Saigon.

Youth camp

Visit www.undergroundreality.com to review Session 2, "Trust in the Trenches." As you see in the video, there are many Christians around the world who are forced into hiding in order to pray and worship God as they choose. **How would you handle a situation like that?**

"After seeing a video of Americans being killed by Vietnamese, and seeing the Vietnamese jumping around so happy about it, standing next to a Vietnamese...and shooting a gun just felt very opposite of what I should be doing. It was like being on the other side, almost."

"Having to run out of a place in pure silence, so we wouldn't get caught by the police, was a wake-up call."

—Wes, Tampa, FL

FRONTLINE DIARIES

Good Morning, Vietnam!!

Hey, everyone!!! This is Jonny B here. Today we went to a place where they had underground tunnels where they hid from the GIs in the Vietnam War. I found it amazing how they made these tunnels and how they could fit in them. . .I was getting mad and sad because they were talking about the U.S. soldiers and how they killed them and how they tortured them. The tour guide said when a Vietinese soldier killed an American they would get an award. I found myself getting really mad. . .people back in the U.S. still seem to hold something against Vietnam. . .We didnt win, maybe that's why... I just want to say thank you to the soldiers that were here.

(Later, with Vietnamese teens at the camp). . .I had no idea what they were saying. . .They're awesome. I just cant explain these people, they are like my best friends. It's like I've known them, but I can't talk to them. . .They have huge hearts. They love to praise God there. I wish people in America would see that.

Jon

Visit www.undergroundreality.com to read more from the Underground Reality Blogs and Reality Blog Archives. The site also provides direction in praying for persecuted Christians in Vietnam and around the world.

Persecution Around the World

Algeria has suffered from civil war for nearly half a century, and tens of thousands have perished. Algeria is 97% Muslim, and a new law restricting Christian evangelism was implemented in March 2006. Those found guilty of "shaking the faith" of a Muslim face punishment of two to five years in prison and a maximum fine of $12,000. This also applies to anyone publishing or keeping literature and/or audio-video materials that threaten the Islamic faith. Non-Muslims are prohibited from practicing their faith outside of government approved buildings.

Visit www.persecution.com for the latest news from the persecuted church around the world.

You'll also find country information, news releases, video clips, and ways you can directly bless persecuted Christians.

Algeria

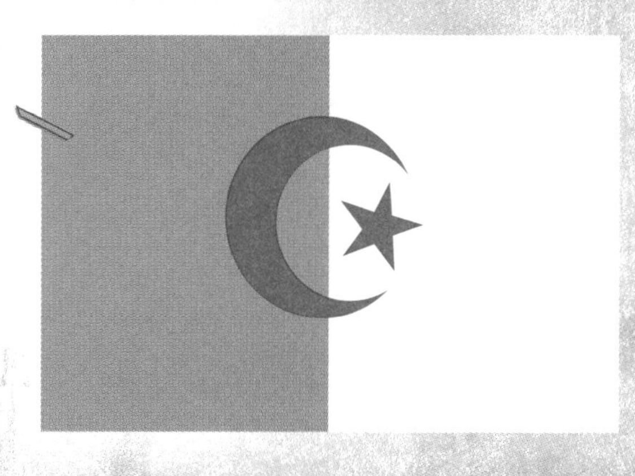

Real-Time Response

Considering the ways that Christians in your culture might experience difficulty, resistance, or opposition for their faith, do you consider such things to be persecution? Why or why not?

What do you think you have in common with the youth in countries like Vietnam?

How do your privileges, freedoms, and experiences as a Christian compare to those of believers in other countries?

Do you think the Vietnamese Christians trust God more, less, or about the same as Christians in America or in other countries with religious freedom? Why?

Do you in any way take for granted your privileges to meet and worship with other Christians? If so, what can you do to show greater appreciation for that privilege?

In Perspective

List ways you might experience opposition for your faith.

List ways that people in places like Vietnam experience persecution for their faith.

Real-Time Response, continued

Why do you think the Vietnamese youth were so thrilled to have the American youth join them?

How do you think persecution might cause you to grow in faith and dependence on God?

The Persecuted Church

The 13% of Egyptians who are considered Christians are treated as second-class citizens. They are denied political representation and face job discrimination. Christian girls have been raped and forced to marry Muslim men. Financial incentives have been offered to convince girls to convert to Islam.

Bold Believers

Missionary Jim Elliot hoped to bring the gospel to an Ecuadorian jungle tribe. The Aucas were violent and had little contact with the outside world. After months of preparation, Jim and his co-workers attempted to win the people's favor by delivering food and gifts to a village. Ironically, after establishing seemingly friendly contact, the Aucas attacked Jim and his associates as they arrived on a beach, killing them with spears. A year later, Jim's widow, Elizabeth, returned to the Ecuadorian jungle to share Jesus with those who killed her husband. Amazingly, she earned their trust. Many placed their trust in Christ. Today, the tribe members fill several churches in Ecuador.

From a human standpoint, it may have seemed at first that Jim Elliot's life and efforts among the Aucas were wasted. But God's plans took a different course, and out of apparent tragedy He worked an amazing transformation in an entire people group. Obstacles and opposition won't stop God from accomplishing something significant in your life. Regardless of the situation, if you remain faithful to reach out to others with Jesus' love and message, God will use your faithful service beyond anything you can imagine.

Today, I Pray

Write a simple prayer, asking God to help you trust Him when facing difficulty, opposition, or uncertainty.

Persecution in Vietnam

Vietnam has long been a hotbed of struggle. Communists had a foothold in North Vietnam and took over all of Vietnam in 1975. To this day, believers are harassed, beaten, and imprisoned for illegally preaching or organizing evangelistic activities. Seeing the role of Christianity in the demise of communism elsewhere, the regime has attempted to either control or wipe out believers. Government efforts have intensifed as churches respond to persecution with growth and outreach.

The Word Thru-the-Week

READ: James 1:5–8

THINK: In what way or area do you need to trust God more?

PRAY: Ask God to keep you from relying on yourself more than on Him.

READ: Matthew 16:1–4 and John 6:26

THINK: Are you waiting for a sign or answer before fully trusting God?

PRAY: Ask God to help you trust Him before you expect answers.

READ: Acts 17:24–27

THINK: Are you making the most of opportunities to influence others for Christ?

PRAY: Thank Jesus for where He has placed you in the world, in history, and for the opportunity to trust Him.

READ: Philippians 2:3–5

THINK: Do you demonstrate a Christlike attitude toward others?

PRAY: Ask God to help you put others before yourself.

READ: 1 John 3:16–18

THINK: How do we demonstrate true love to others, and why is this vital?

PRAY: Ask God to help you recognize tangible ways to show His love.

READ: Hebrews 11:13–16 and Romans 13:12–14

THINK: Do you live as if your home is heaven on earth? Would you say you have put off the deeds of darkness in exchange for the armor of light?

PRAY: Pray that your actions draw positive attention to Jesus.

Remember to go to www.undergroundreality.com and www.persecution.com for direction and inspiration regarding how to pray daily for persecuted Christians around the world.

I Dare You

This week's mission, should you choose to accept it: Think of one area of your life in which people, circumstances, or even your own thinking are hindering you from doing what God wants you to do. Perhaps you've hesitated to act because of unexpected resistance, fear, or the desire for a "sign" from God. Unless it's medically unwise for you to do so, fast at least one meal this week. Instead of eating, use the time to pray for God's direction. If He's already given you direction, pray for discipline and strength to take action. Perhaps God is leading you to get involved in a ministry at church, start a campus club at school, pray for someone who needs a miracle or talk to someone about your faith. Take a bold step, trusting God to lead you into a new adventure. If something is getting in the way of your devotion to Christ, resolve that issue once and for all. If it means changing your lifestyle or giving something up, remember that God's reward will surpass your sacrifice.

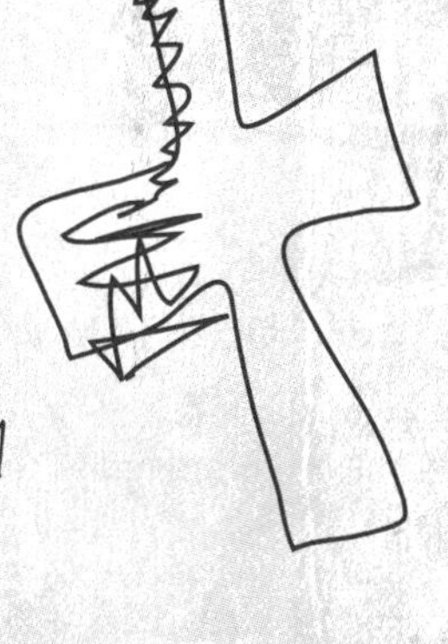

Listen to SonicFlood's song "Look to Love" at www.undergroundreality.com this week. During the next session, there will be a contest to see who can remember the lyrics the best.

Session #3

No-Fear/No-Hate Christianity

WHAT's the Point?

Jesus' followers must demonstrate a positive difference that enhances society, reflects what He's like, and influences others to follow Him.

WHY Does It Matter?

Most people's impression of Jesus comes from what they see and encounter through those who claim to follow Him.

HOW Can I Live It?

Live in a way that accurately reflects Jesus' character and inspires others to trust Him.

Bible Basis

"Blessed are those who are persecuted because of righteousness, for theirs is the kingdom of heaven. Blessed are you when people insult you, persecute you and falsely say all kinds of evil against you because of me. Rejoice and be glad, because great is your reward in heaven, for in the same way they persecuted the prophets who were before you. You are the salt of the earth. But if the salt loses its saltiness, how can it be made salty again? It is no longer good for anything, except to be thrown out and trampled by men. You are the light of the world. A city on a hill cannot be hidden. Neither do people light a lamp and put it under a bowl. Instead they put it on its stand, and it gives light to everyone in the house. In the same way, let your light shine before men, that they may see your good deeds and praise your Father in heaven" (Matthew 5:10–16).

"Courage is not the absence of fear, but rather the judgment that something else is more important than fear."

—Ambrose Redmoon (1933–1996)

The Challenge

What are you afraid of? While it may be difficult to admit fears, as a follower of Jesus, you don't have to be a slave to fear. **First John 4:18** says that "perfect love drives out fear." This means that if you're in a right relationship with God, you don't have to fear His judgment, but neither do you have to fear anyone or anything in this life (**see Psalm 27:1**). This means that you're free to face fearful situations with boldness, and you are liberated to love "unlovely" people—unlovely in the sense of how they may treat you. Think about a time when someone insulted you, gossiped or lied about you. You probably weren't happy about it. In fact, you may have been furious at those who attempted to hurt you. But Jesus says that when you are the victim of this kind of persecution—particularly because of your faith in Him—you should rejoice (**Matthew 5:11–12**). That's because when people mistreat you, it gives you a chance to respond with God's love and to stand out in a positive way for Christ.

Read Luke 6:27–36. According to this passage, how are you to respond toward those who hate, oppose, or mistreat you because of your faith? Why is it important to respond this way?

It would be easy to hate those who mistreat you. Fear and hate—two of the most intense and potentially destructive emotions—often work together. But there is something more powerful: love. As you become more like Jesus, it's possible to express genuine love for those who oppose or attempt to harm you. This demonstrates Christ's character and honors His command. This is vital because people who don't know Christ are unlikely to turn to Him unless they experience His love from those who follow Him. For this reason, make every effort to show compassion to people who have given you difficulty.

What are some practical ways to "love your enemies" (Luke 6:27), and what is Jesus' promise when you do?

Read 1 Peter 4:12–14. What attitude should you have toward suffering for Christ? Why do you think Jesus asks us to rejoice in the midst of persecution?

Read Luke 12:4–7. Even in the midst of the most intense persecution, what do you not have to fear and why?

Because of God's love and care, you're free not only to love those who mistreat or hate you, but to actually influence them for God. **Read this week's key text, Matthew 5:10–16. Why do you think Jesus uses salt and light to describe His followers**

Salt is a flavor enhancer, a preservative, a healing agent. It also creates thirst. Through their faith and lifestyle, Christians enhance society, bring healing to hurting people, and create spiritual thirst, giving others a desire to know God. Christians also provide light in a spiritually dark world. Their lives stand out in a positive, illuminating way (**see 1 Peter 2:9**). As a Christian, you have the privilege of reflecting the life, love, and light of Jesus—particularly through times of trouble and opposition. **How can you be "salt and light" to people who typically give you a difficult time?**

In order to truly show people who Jesus is and what He is like, you must follow His example of servanthood (**see John 13:14–16**). By serving people, we reflect Christ's humility and demonstrate His compassion. We break down barriers of resistance and opposition to the truth of God's Word and the reality of Jesus' life-changing power. **What are some practical ways we can serve and help meet people's needs in a way that may influence them for Christ?**

Live, from Vietnam

Pastor Quang

Over the past three weeks, you've watched eight teens embark on a journey to communist-controlled Vietnam where they were exposed to life in the underground church. Last week left off as the team was rushed out of a secret worship meeting. This week they traveled to a disguised Christian youth camp, which police would close down if they discovered its true purpose.

The video also introduced you to Pastor Quang, who shared how he decided to enter the ministry. After seeing fear in church leaders following a police raid that killed one of the Christians, Quang determined, "For me and my generation, we will not be afraid. So I dedicated myself to serving the Lord." In the midst of persecution, Pastor Quang become salt and light in a spiritually dark environment. That decision cost him dearly.

"When God called me, I knew I must pay a price for the Lord."
—Pastor Quang

How would you feel toward authorities if they destroyed your church, imprisoned you or your leaders multiple times, and made several assassination attempts? Would you be tempted to retaliate? Why or why not?

Watch this week's session on www.undergroundreality.com.

To find out what happened when the police showed up at the camp, click on the Trip Reports and read the mid-week report.

"There are only 30 people in this church, but they are forced to move their place of worship every few months because someone will find out where they're meeting…it's just heartbreaking."

—Brad, Sydney Australia, FL

in His name we pray

Undergound Reality: Vietnam

In May 2006, police armed with nightsticks, numchucks, and cattle prods raided Pastor Nguyen Hong Quang's house church. Many members were beaten. Pastor Quang and ten others were arrested.

FRONTLINE DIARIES

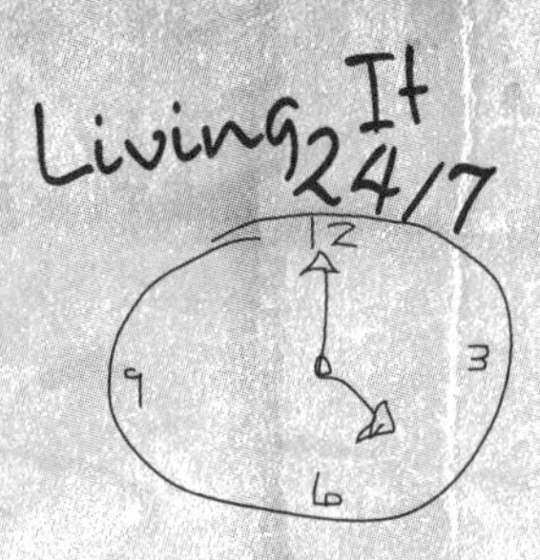

I didn't know that I was coming here to learn, I had no idea...I thought I was here to do the work...But I had a complete mindset of how a lot of things were when I came here, and I didn't want to think any different...I sort of sheltered myself from that kind of thing at home...I never wanted to see the uncomfortable or the bad. I was always good at seeing the sugar-coated way.

...Persecution where I come from is being made fun of and being shunned away from the group. Persecution here is having your family taken away or killed and everything taken from you and being thrown in prison...It's really put my Christian walk in perspective. I do all the right things, but I'm not living it. But these people are living it 24/7.

Wes

Read more blogs at www.undergroundreality.com Look for the Underground Reality Blogs and Reality Blog Archives. Plus you'll find ways to pray for persecuted Christians in Vietnam and around the world.

Persecution Around the World

Belarus became an independent state after the collapse of the Soviet Union, but failed policy has crippled economic development. In 2002 a law came into effect that strictly limits or prohibits all unregistered religious activity, even in private homes. Religious literature is subject to censorship, and all religious organizations are required to re-register with the government every two years. Pastors and religious leaders have been jailed for things like conducting worship in their homes and training leadership without government approval. A judge even ordered a large church to sell its property to city authorities for a fraction of its value.

Read the latest news from the persecuted church at www.persecution.com.

You'll also find country information, news releases, video clips, and ways you can directly bless persecuted Christians.

In Perspective

List practical ways you can be salt and light—a positive influence for Christ in your culture. Consider specific people and places.

Ask God to show you how and when you can take specific action with these ideas. Circle one that you can do this week.

The Persecuted Church

In southern Kyrgyzstan, angry mobs, led by Islamic clerics, have entered worship services or homes of church planters and given Christians an ultimatum to leave—or their church or home will be burned and their children and wives defiled. In several locations, wives were raped when church leaders didn't flee.

Real-Time Response

In the video, one of the Vietnamese Christians said that the church can exist, but organizing events requires government approval, and the request is typically met with rejection.

How do you think your faith would be affected without the opportunity to meet freely with other Christians?

In the video, Pastor Quang said that when God called him, he knew he had to "pay the price." What do you think he meant by that?

How can Christians' attitudes and actions affect people's impressions of God in both positive and negative ways?

It has been said that the world will not care how much we know, until they know how much we care. How can you show Christ's compassion and reach your generation for Christ?

The Church in Vietnam

Believers view church registration as compromise because the government would restrict them so much. But the government views failure to register as illegal, forcing the church underground. In 2005, the Vietnamese government promised to allow greater religious freedom. But little has changed. Only a handful of Christians have been released from prison, and many have been forced to renounce their faith.

Bold Believers

Known as the Ugandan martyrs, thirty-two young pages in the court of King Mwanga were burned to death on June 3, 1886, for refusing to renounce Christ. In the months that followed, many more Christians died for their faith. Realizing that the believers put loyalty to Christ ahead of loyalty to the king, Mwanga vowed to wipe out Christianity, threatening to execute anyone who even approached a Christian mission. But his plan backfired. The martyrs' example inspired many to seek instruction from the remaining Christians. As a result, most of the missionary work in Uganda was carried out by national leaders rather than by white missionaries, and Christianity spread rapidly. Today, Uganda has the largest percentage of professing Christians of any African nation.

Do you ever feel as if your life and faith will have little or no influence on others?

Perhaps this feeling is strongest when you're facing rejection and opposition for your faith. But remember, those times present opportunities for your faith to shine. In fact, your most powerful and lasting influence can stem from times when you endure opposition for Christ and even show kindness to those who cause it.

Ugandan grandmother

Today, I Pray

Consider individuals that you might have a difficult time loving and reaching for Christ. Write a brief prayer for these individuals—and for yourself—that God will give you a supernatural love for them and that He would enable you to influence them for Christ.

The Word Thru-the-Week

READ: Acts 16:16–29
THINK: How will you respond to insult and opposition?
PRAY: Pray that Jesus' character would be evident in your life.

READ: 2 Corinthians 4:3–6
THINK: Who is your real enemy and what are you called to preach?
PRAY: Ask Jesus to help you be light in your sphere of influence.

READ: Matthew 5:11-12
THINK: What attitude are you challenged to have through suffering? Why are we blessed when suffering for His sake?
PRAY: Thank Jesus for the opportunity to share in His suffering. Pray that you would view others with Jesus' compassion.

READ: 1 Thessalonians 5:15
THINK: How do you treat those who give you trouble?
PRAY: Ask God to help you show kindness to those who mistreat you.

READ: Matthew 10:28 and 1 Thessalonians 2:1–6
THINK: Are you more concerned with people's approval or God's?
PRAY: Ask Jesus to relieve your fear of what people might say and do.

READ: Hebrews 12:1–3
THINK: Look at your responses to the "In Perspective" page in Session 1. What have you done to lay aside things that could distract you from fulfilling God's purposes and influencing others to follow Christ?
PRAY: Pray that your focus remains on Jesus and that His joy is evident in your life.

Remember to go to www.undergroundreality.com and www.persecution.com. You will find ways to pray daily for persecuted Christians around the world.

I Dare You

This week's mission, should you choose to accept it: Think of someone with whom you don't normally associate or may even consider an enemy—one with whom you've had difficulty in the past. Make a specific effort to find a reason to thank or compliment that person. Also, do something to show kindness to that person. If you have a lingering conflict with that individual, attempt to resolve the issue. This may mean offering a sincere apology or extending forgiveness. As an act of good faith and friendship, invite that person to join you at a youth event or casual get-together with friends.

Make a point to have a more positive relationship with this person from now on.

Real Life, Real Pain Session #4

"When you have nothing left but God, then you become aware that God is enough."

—Maude Royden (1876–1956)

WHAT's the Point?

When experiencing persecution for Christ, we can trust Him for the strength and insight to respond in a God-honoring way.

WHY Does It Matter?

Opposition and persecution provide Christ's followers with opportunities to demonstrate His character and influence others to trust Him.

HOW Can I Live It?

When you rely on God, He will use your troubles and the opposition you face to grow your faith, build your character, and inspire spiritual victories.

Why does God allow His followers to suffer persecution, and what good can come from it?

Bible Basis

"I am sending you out like sheep among wolves. Therefore be as shrewd as snakes and as innocent as doves. Be on your guard against men; they will hand you over to the local councils and flog you in their synagogues. On my account you will be brought before governors and kings as witnesses to them and to the Gentiles. But when they arrest you, do not worry about what to say or how to say it. At that time you will be given what to say, for it will not be you speaking, but the Spirit of your Father speaking through you. Brother will betray brother to death, and a father his child; children will rebel against their parents and have them put to death. All men will hate you because of me, but he who stands firm to the end will be saved. When you are persecuted in one place, flee to another. I tell you the truth, you will not finish going through the cities of Israel before the Son of Man comes" (Matthew 10:16–23).

The Challenge

"How can a loving God allow suffering and evil to continue?" "Why do bad things happen to good people?" "Where is God when tragedy strikes?" Though these questions take many forms, they all represent a struggle to reconcile the idea of an all-loving, all-powerful God with all the bad things people see going on around them. Some look at tragedy and conclude that if God is all-loving, He must not be all-powerful or He would prevent suffering. Others assume that if God is all-powerful but allows the innocent to suffer, then He must not be loving. However, love does not necessarily contradict or eliminate suffering.

Questioning how a loving God could allow evil and suffering shows a misunderstanding of what is normal and what is exceptional in the world. Because humankind has rebelled against God and chosen their own way over His way, sin and evil have taken hold and turned the world upside down and backward from the way God created it. The fact that any good exists at all—and can even come out of suffering—is proof of God's love and patience toward a world that continues to defy Him. **Read Romans 8:28–39. Why do you think God allows suffering, pain, and persecution in His followers' lives?**

For those who face persecution, what is true about God's love?

Jesus endured the ultimate suffering in order to accomplish the ultimate good and to make spiritual salvation available to all (see Isaiah 53; 1 Peter 3:18). He also taught His followers to expect difficulty in this life (see John 15:18–21; 16:33). Faithfulness to God doesn't guarantee freedom from trouble, pain, and suffering. The Bible provides numerous examples of godly people who suffered for a variety of reasons. Among these are King David, Job, the prophet Jeremiah, and the apostle Paul. Consider the story of Joseph (see Genesis 37, 39—41), who was mistreated, betrayed, enslaved, wrongfully accused, imprisoned, and seemingly forgotten. But God ultimately blessed and exalted Joseph beyond anything he could have imagined. The question is not whether we'll experience pain and hardship in life, but rather, what will we do when we experience it. Trials will make us bitter or better. The choice is up to you. **Read Romans 5:3–5 and James 1:2–4. What character traits can you ask God to develop in you as you experience suffering and hard times as a Christian? Why are these traits important?**

Painful experiences can bring destruction or growth—depending on a person's response. The problem is that most people spend their time trying to figure out why they are suffering before deciding how to respond. Since we may never fully understand the reasons, the Bible steers us away from focusing on the source or reason for suffering. Instead, we should concentrate on how we can grow closer to God through it. One way to grow closer to God while strengthening your faith during tough times is through prayer. **Read David's prayer in Psalm 5:1–4 and then read Psalm 9:9–14. What assurances do those who know God have during times of trouble and oppression?**

Read this week's key text, Matthew 10:16–23. Why do you not have to fear confrontation from those who oppose your faith? What opportunities can be found in suffering for Christ?

Read Romans 8:17–18. What hope do you have if you share in Christ's sufferings?

Persecution in Vietnam

Two Degar Christians were killed in prison in July 2006, and in late August 2006, a Montagnard Christian died following alleged torture in prison. The Montagnard/Degar people live in the highland jungles of Vietnam.

Live, from Vietnam

Last week you arrived at a camp with the eight teens on a Bible-smuggling mission to Vietnam. One of the Vietnamese teens at the camp was named Nyung. This young girl experienced firsthand what it costs to be a Christian in her country. She had received Christ at age twelve and was put in jail as a result. Since that time, she has been imprisoned a number of times, often threatened, even physically abused for not revealing information about the church. This story had a profound and emotional impact on Taani, a mission team member from Sydney, Australia. Summer, the team's translator said that Taani changed from that point on, talking and acting differently. Her empathy for Nyung had a powerful impact on the entire team.

Taani with Nyung, and Summer

"The tribal girl (Nyung)... was so touched because somebody wanted to hear her story, to capture that and to tell the world what she'd been through."

—Summer, team translator

Why do you think Taani was so gripped by emotion after hearing Nyung's story? How did you feel as you heard it?

"Yes, I was very scared during the torture and investigations. They asked me many questions about the underground church, and if I don't tell them they will beat me up... They beat me up and almost raped me."

—Nyung, age 16

Watch this week's session on www.undergroundreality.com

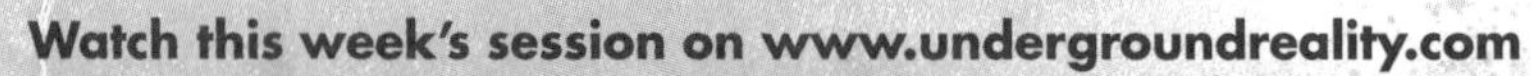

FRONTLINE DIARIES

Hi, all! Well, what an amazing last couple of days we've had! Yesterday we went to the big youth camp, with heaps of kids from all over Vietnam. It was incredible to see them all having fun and singing to the same God that we worship. The definite highlight of my day was talking to a Vietnamese girl, sixteen years old, like me. Through the translator, I found out that she became a Christian when she was twelve and since then... she has been put in prison numerous times and has been tortured in many different ways. She has been beaten, kicked, stabbed with electric prods, forced to eat raw pork, and almost raped. Even during all these times, she refused to deny God... The reality of her situation really hit hard, and it brought me to tears. Although we read the stories in books... it is so much different hearing it in real life, and talking to them face to face... I was again brought to tears this morning when we had to sneak away from the campsite as fast as we could. The fact that this happens to them all the time makes me realize how much I take for granted.

Taani XOXO

Read more blogs at www.undergroundreality.com
Look for the Underground Reality Blogs and Reality Blog Archives. Plus you'll find ways to pray for persecuted Christians in Vietnam and around the world.

Persecution Around the World

Bhutan was isolated from the outside world until the communist takeover of China in 1949. The government's isolationist policies further reinforced the hold of Buddhism, which comprises 72% of the religious population. Another 23% are Hindu, while less than 5% are Christian. All public worship and evangelism by non-Buddhists is illegal in Bhutan. When Bhutanese are discovered to have converted to Christianity, they are denied government benefits—including public education. Christians have been fired from jobs and some have been expelled from the country. Others have been imprisoned without trial and sentenced to years in jail.

Read the latest news from the persecuted church at www.persecution.com.

You'll also find country information, news releases, video clips, and ways you can directly bless persecuted Christians.

Real-Time Response

Did Nyung's testimony inspire your faith in God or cause you to question it, and why?

the Salt and Light

At the end of this week's video, Summer, the team translator, had a severe reaction to ant bites and could hardly breathe. What did this experience bring out of the team members? Why does it sometimes take an intense crisis for people to depend on God?

In what situations do you feel weak and powerless, and how could you better exercise your faith during those times?

Real-Time Response, continued

What impact is your faith making on those around you, particularly when you face trouble or opposition? How could you be more influential for Christ during such times?

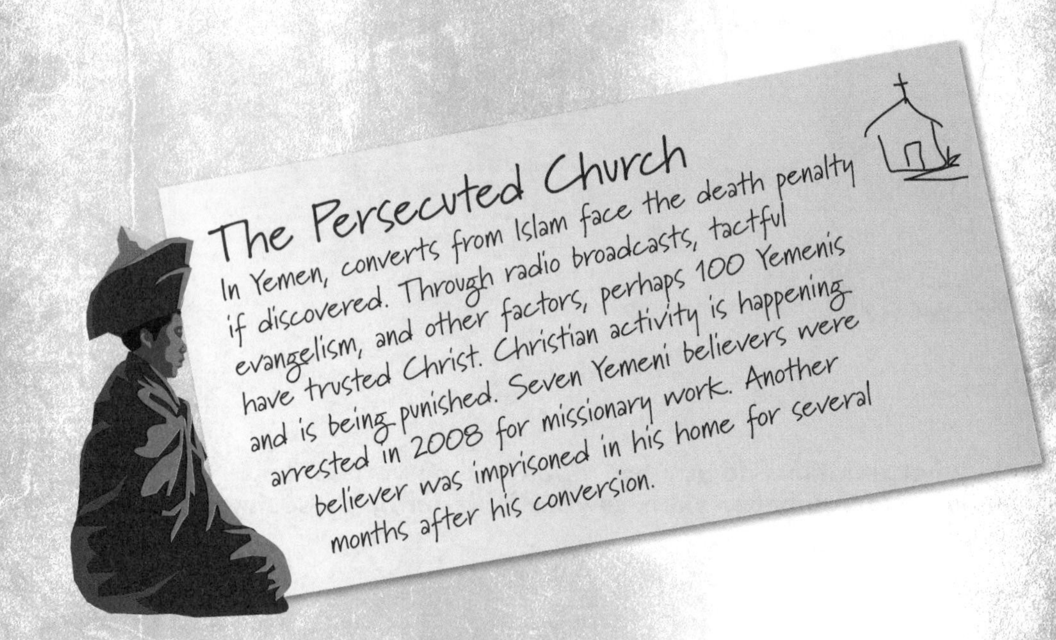

The Persecuted Church

In Yemen, converts from Islam face the death penalty if discovered. Through radio broadcasts, tactful evangelism, and other factors, perhaps 100 Yemenis have trusted Christ. Christian activity is happening and is being punished. Seven Yemeni believers were arrested in 2008 for missionary work. Another believer was imprisoned in his home for several months after his conversion.

In Perspective

What things would you most like to be remembered for by the end of your high school years?

What actions, behaviors, and disciplines will it take for you to gain that reputation?

Bold Believers

Tens of thousands of North Korean Christians have endured torture in concentration camps. Many have been executed. Prisoners who react in horror to the executions are often punished with electrical shock. Others are crammed into solitary confinement containers so cramped that their legs become permanently paralyzed. There is a particularly disturbing story about several Christians who were working in a smelting factory operated by the prison. Because these Christians refused to deny their faith, the prison leaders poured molten iron on them in the factory and they died instantly. Yet something remarkable is happening. The suffering of North Korean Christians is emboldening many of their countrymen, and many are escaping to China or South Korea where they are turning to Christianity.

To many who witnessed and experienced these atrocities, the suffering of the North Korean Christians no doubt seemed senseless. Who would have thought, however, that such cruelty and terror would inspire such boldness in others. You may never have to endure the type of pain and suffering described here, but never underestimate God's ability to turn tragedy into triumph. If you are willing to endure pain and rejection for Him, God can use your influence to inspire others to trust Christ as well.

Today, I Pray

Write a simple prayer, asking God for the strength to endure persecution in a way that inspires others to trust Christ.

Conversion in Vietnam

Hundreds of thousands have turned to Christ in the past fifteen years. They baptize at night in streams. Many walk days to obtain and distribute Bibles. A number have been imprisoned, and some have been forced to renounce their faith.

The Word Thru-the-Week

READ: 2 Timothy 3:12–13
THINK: What might it say about your faith if you're not experiencing opposition?
PRAY: Ask God to help you pursue His plans, regardless of the cost.

READ: 1 Corinthians 9:24–27
THINK: Do you allow tough times to make you more mature?
PRAY: Ask God for added strength and joy through trying times.

READ: Psalm 17:6–9; 18:2
THINK: Do you view trials as an opportunity to trust God?
PRAY: Give God thanks for being your refuge and defender.

READ: Acts 4:1–13
THINK: Do you consider persecution an opportunity to reflect Jesus' character?
PRAY: Ask the Holy Spirit for insight in responding to opposition in a way that honors God.

READ: Romans 8:16–18
THINK: Are you more focused on temporary trials or on eternal glory?
PRAY: Give thanks to God for making you His child and thank Jesus for the opportunity to share His sufferings.

READ: Psalm 62:1–2 and 1 Peter 1:3–9
THINK: Where do you look for relief and hope during difficulties?
PRAY: Thank Jesus for the ultimate hope He provides.

Remember to go to www.undergroundreality.com and www.persecution.com. You will find ways to pray daily for persecuted Christians around the world.

I Dare You

This week's mission, should you choose to accept it: Consider someone who is experiencing a difficulty or trial to which you can relate through personal experience. The issue may be physical, emotional, spiritual, relational, financial, academic, and so on. Offer any encouragement you feel is appropriate and helpful.

Let the person know that you're thinking of him and will be praying for the situation. If he is comfortable allowing you to do so, pray for him in person. In addition, offer any practical assistance you can to help the person in dealing with the difficulty. Encourage him to trust God and rely on Him like never before during this time.

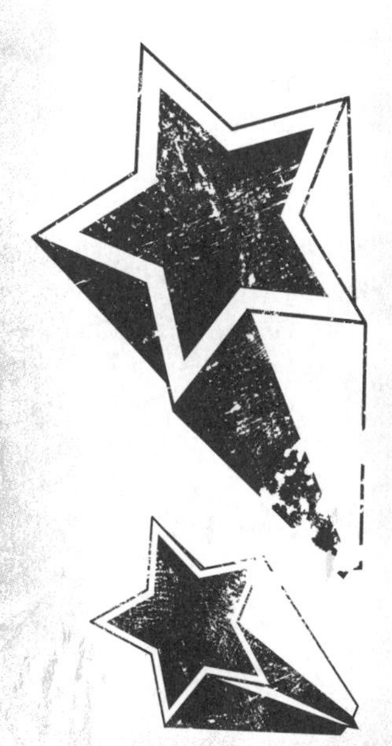

Session #5

Hell's Most Wanted List

"He is no fool who gives what he cannot keep to gain what he cannot lose."

—Jim Elliot (1927–1956)

WHAT's the Point?

Following Christ puts you on "hell's most wanted list," but it also brings the reward of knowing God and fulfilling His purposes.

WHY Does It Matter?

Unless we're willing to pay the price of identifying with Jesus, we will not experience His purposes nor influence others to follow Him.

HOW Can I Live It?

Boldly identify with Jesus and aim to fulfill God's purposes for your life, regardless of the cost.

What is it costing you to follow Christ and to fulfill His purposes?

Bible Basis

Then he said to them all: "If anyone would come after me, he must deny himself and take up his cross daily and follow me. For whoever wants to save his life will lose it, but whoever loses his life for me will save it. What good is it for a man to gain the whole world, and yet lose or forfeit his very self ? If anyone is ashamed of me and my words, the Son of Man will be ashamed of him when he comes in his glory and in the glory of the Father and of the holy angels" (Luke 9:23–26).

The Challenge

During the course of your lifetime—even as a student—your name will appear on a variety of lists—some desirable and some not. For example, you may be proud to make the honor roll, the starting basketball roster, or the musical callback list. However, you would not be so pleased to make a detention list, worst dressed list, or a gang's hit list. There are certain things with which you'd rather not be associated, while there are other things with which you're proud to identify. But here's the real issue: Many things worth accomplishing or identifying with don't come easily. So what is it costing you to follow Christ? It's not a matter of earning a relationship with God by your own efforts. Jesus paid that price with His own life, and God provides salvation as a free gift to those who entrust their lives to Christ. But continuing to live for Jesus in this God-defying world will cost you considerably.

Read this week's key Bible text, Luke 9:23–26. What do you think it means to deny yourself and take up your cross (v. 23)?

When Jesus calls us to "deny" ourselves, He's not just talking about what we leave behind or give up. He's more concerned with where we're going. Rather than limiting the possibilities, serving Jesus opens a world of possibilities. **Read John 12:24–25. What does it mean to lose your life and how can that help you find it?**

Identifying with Christ makes you a target of a very real enemy. **Read 1 Peter 5:8–9 and Revelation 12:9. Who is the real source of opposition to Jesus' followers? In what ways is this opposition evident in your own life and in the world at large?**

Following Jesus puts you on "hell's most wanted list." Satan will use all sorts of schemes and attacks to entice you to lay down your cross, disassociate from Jesus, and return to your old way of life.

Read Luke 10:19–20. What kind of authority do Jesus' followers have and what should they rejoice about?

Originally, hell was made for Satan and his evil forces—not for people. Only those who fail to put their trust in Jesus end up in hell. The devil and his demons want to take as many people with them as possible, but we overcome them by putting ourselves aside, identifying with Jesus, and spreading His message. **Read Revelation 3:5; 20:11–15. What will eventually happen to the devil? Where will the names of those who overcome be listed? What will this mean for them?**

Press Release: 7/7/07

"The president of Vietnam calls evangelical Christians lawbreakers and says they should be punished. But the reality is these are simply Christians who want the freedom to worship God according to their conscience. They love their country; they pray for their government leaders. These aren't troublemakers or rebels, yet they are arrested, beaten, and imprisoned."

— Todd Nettleton, spokesperson for The Voice of the Martyrs

Live, from Vietnam

This week the teens on the Vietnam mission team were rushed out of the youth camp just ahead of the police. Later that day, they visit a Bible college, which took a risk simply to have them there. The property is frequently under police surveillance and the living conditions are meager and modest, to say the least. As many as two hundred students are packed into an extremely limited space with one small kitchen, two shared bathrooms, and an individual limit of one backpack-size piece of luggage. For safety reasons, the students can't come and go freely. This is their world for four years.

"It's really convicting, actually, because we don't even want to give up for church, but they sacrifice it all and don't think twice about it...They were so single-minded in their pursuit of Christ... Your heart just totally has to change. You have to die to yourself completely... You have to give all of your dreams and all of your desires to Christ."

—Bethany, Bartlesville, OK

Bible college

What did you think as you saw how the Bible college students lived? Could you handle living in such cramped and isolated conditions? Why or why not?

Watch this week's session on www.undergroundreality.com

FRONTLINE DIARIES

This morning was awesome.

Before breakfast we went for worship. I learned a Vietnamese song "We Cry Holy." It was pretty sweet...

...P.S. I think I ate dog for breakfast this morning because it was unlike any meat that I've ever tasted in my life. The kids at the camp amazed me by how they took to us right away. Back home we'd all be in our own little cliques, and the camp would be more of a popularity contest than it would be about God. That's the total opposite of the Vietnamese Bible camp. ...I met girls younger than myself who have gone through more than I probably will in a lifetime, and yet they were stronger than ever in their faith... It's absolutely amazing... I always knew about persecution... We've had flags hanging in our church auditorium for so long, and almost every week we pray for persecuted Christians. But it didn't become real until I came to Vietnam... I now realize how incredibly privileged I am to be able to express my faith freely, without fear of going to jail... I'll never again take my faith and what I'm allowed to do with it for granted.

Shannon

Read more blogs at www.undergroundreality.com

Look for the Underground Reality Blogs and Reality Blog Archives. Plus you'll find ways to pray for persecuted Christians in Vietnam and around the world.

Persecution Around the World

China was declared the People's Republic of China in 1949 by Chairman Mao Zedong, who quickly sought to purge society of anything that promoted religion. Since then, China's human rights record has been one of the worst in the world. More Christians are detained or imprisoned in China than in any other country. Confiscation of church property and Bibles is common. The house church movement, which comprises about 90% of China's Christians, endures horrendous persecution. On July 4, 2006, prominent house church leader Pastor Zhang Rongliang was sentenced to seven and a half years in prison for traveling overseas to a missions conference. Later that month, several thousand anti-riot police in three hundred military vehicles converged on a newly constructed church. Several hundred Christians were beaten and many arrested.

Read the latest news from the persecuted church at www.persecution.com.

You'll also find country information, news releases, video clips, and ways you can directly bless persecuted Christians.

Real-Time Response

One teen noted how "single-minded" the Vietnamese students were in pursuit of Christ. **What does this mean? Would you describe yourself as single-minded at this point? Explain.**

What's your "mark of identity? What are you known for among your peers? What do they think of when they think of you?

Perhaps your identity is linked to a personal achievement, favorite activity, character trait—or even a personal failure. As Christians, it's important that we don't let our identity as followers of Jesus get buried beneath other less important things. Our goal is to live in such a way that people will think of Jesus when they think of us.

In what ways is your life different from those who don't know Christ? In what ways is your life in need of change because it's too much like those who don't know Christ?

If you're not completely certain your name is written on heaven's list—in the Book of Life—you can be sure from this moment on. Pray this simple prayer from your heart:

Salvation Prayer

Lord Jesus, I've gone my own way and sinned against you. Have mercy on me and forgive my sin. I believe You are God's Son who died in my place, then rose from the dead with the authority to give me a new life. Thanks for making me a child of God and putting my name in Your Book of Life. I turn from my sins and surrender my life to Your purposes. Give me the boldness to confess my faith in You to others. I ask this in Your name, Jesus. Amen.

In Perspective

What are some action steps or attitude adjustments you could make to identify with Jesus more boldly and effectively?

What are some things you could do to follow Christ more intimately?

Bold Believers

Following the capture of a mission station during China's Boxer Rebellion in 1900, students were forced to choose between life and death. Rebels blocked all but one gate and laid a cross on the ground in front of it. If students would trample over the cross, they could gain freedom; otherwise, they would face a firing squad. Seven terrified students were allowed to escape, running over the cross and through the gate. But the eighth student knelt beside the cross to pray for strength, got up, and walked around the cross. She died in front of the firing squad—along with the other ninety-two students who followed her example.

These students were targeted by the enemy because of their devotion to Jesus, and they were put to the ultimate test. But they were willing to identify with their Savior at any cost. They paid a price that most of us may never be called to endure. Yet Christ calls all who follow Him to lay down their lives—to do something that may often be more difficult than dying for Him—that is, taking up your cross daily for Him. That means putting selfish interests aside and enduring the opposition that stems from following Christ and spreading His message. By taking a bold stand for Jesus—particularly through times of difficulty and pain—you can identify with Jesus and inspire others to trust Him.

Today, I Pray

Write a simple prayer, asking God for boldness to identify with Christ and follow His purposes, regardless of the conditions and costs.

The Word Thru-the-Week

READ: 1 Peter 5:8–9 and Revelation 12:9

THINK: How can you avoid being deceived by Satan's tactics?

PRAY: Pray for alertness and self-control in resisting and overcoming the devil's schemes.

READ: 1 Timothy 2:3–4 and Colossians 4:2–3

THINK: Have you asked God to open doors for you to tell others about Jesus?

PRAY: Ask God to prepare people's hearts for the gospel.

READ: 1 Corinthians 2:2–5; 2 Corinthians 5:20

THINK: Are you known for your relationship with Jesus? Are you doing your own thing, or God's?

PRAY: Pray for strength and devotion to be unashamed of Christ.

READ: 1 Thessalonians 5:22 and 2 Timothy 2:22

THINK: What does following Jesus have to do with fleeing temptation? How do you do this?

PRAY: Ask for wisdom and discipline to avoid tempting situations.

READ: 1 Timothy 6:11 and Colossians 3:1–17

THINK: How does following Jesus relate to pursuing righteousness? What does this mean, and how do you do it?

PRAY: Ask God to help you focus more on the things He wants you to do so you don't get caught up in things you should avoid.

READ: Acts 20:24

THINK: Are you spending your life on God's purposes or your own?

PRAY: Ask God to help you die to selfish desires so you can be fruitful for Him.

Remember to go to www.undergroundreality.com and www.persecution.com this week. You will find ways to pray daily for persecuted Christians around the world.

I Dare You

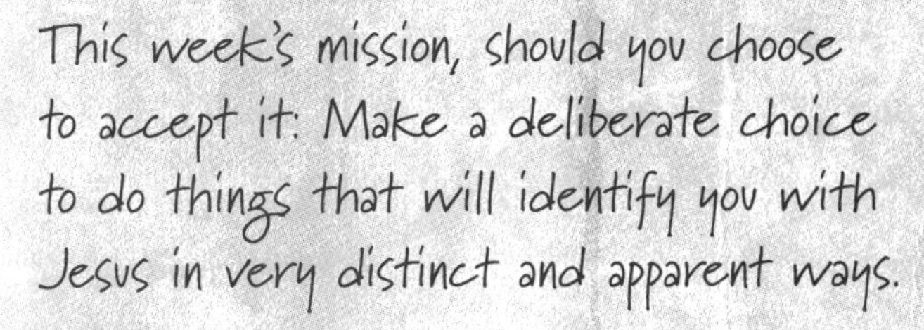

This week's mission, should you choose to accept it: Make a deliberate choice to do things that will identify you with Jesus in very distinct and apparent ways.

This could involve wearing a shirt with a bold Christian message, carrying your Bible and using it during study hall, doing a class project on a Christian theme, inviting people to a youth ministry event, and so on.

Do something out of your ordinary routine, not for show, but out of genuine devotion to Christ and a desire to identify with Him. Be prepared for your actions to spark spiritual conversations and to open doors for you to share your faith in Christ.

Session #6

What's Your Breaking Point?

"Ministry that costs nothing accomplishes nothing."
—John Henry Jowett (1864–1923)

WHAT's the Point?

God provides the support and strategies to help us endure even the most intense persecution.

WHY Does It Matter?

Relying on God through persecution gives us the opportunity to honor Him, grow in our faith, and demonstrate His love to others.

HOW Can I Live It?

Rely on God for the patience, joy, love, and wisdom to endure and honor Him through difficulty and persecution.

How can we remain faithful to God through extreme pain and persecution?

Bible Basis

Love must be sincere. Hate what is evil; cling to what is good. Be devoted to one another in brotherly love. Honor one another above your selves. Never be lacking in zeal, but keep your spiritual fervor, serving the Lord. Be joyful in hope, patient in affliction, faithful in prayer. Share with God's people who are in need. Practice hospitality. Bless those who persecute you; bless and do not curse. Rejoice with those who rejoice; mourn with those who mourn. Live in harmony with one another. Do not be proud, but be willing to associate with people of low position. Do not be conceited. Do not repay anyone evil for evil. Be careful to do what is right in the eyes of everybody. If it is possible, as far as it depends on you, live at peace with everyone. Do not take revenge, my friends, but leave room for God's wrath, for it is written: "It is mine to avenge; I will repay," says the Lord. On the contrary: "If your enemy is hungry, feed him; if he is thirsty, give him something to drink. In doing this, you will heap burning coals on his head." Do not be overcome by evil, but overcome evil with good (Romans 12:9–21).

The Challenge

By now, you've no doubt gained a greater awareness of the persecuted church around the world. But while you may be inspired by what you've heard and read, you may feel inadequate. Perhaps you wonder if you could stand up to persecution—or would your faith crumble under the pressure? The good news is that God provides strategies to help us stand strong through intense opposition. You'll see that it is not a matter of your own strength and endurance, but of God's faithfulness to those who trust Him. In Hebrews 13:5–6, God reminds us, "'Never will I leave you; never will I forsake you." So we can say with confidence, "The Lord is my helper; I will not be afraid. What can man do to me?"

Romans 12:9–21 provides insights and strategies for enduring hard times. Romans 12:12 says, "Be joyful in hope, patient in affliction, faithful in prayer." What is the biggest challenge to being "joyful in hope" in any situation?

What do you think it means to be "patient in affliction"? Does this mean we must always endure pain and abuse without response or retaliation? Why or why not?

Why is being "faithful in prayer" vital for patience and hope?

Read Romans 12:14. This verse tells us to bless those who persecute us, even to meet their practical needs. What are some practical ways to bless those who persecute you?

A vital discipline to keep in mind as you seek to stand firm in faith, regardless of the circumstances, is to rely on God and use wisdom in trying times. Read 1 Corinthians 10:12–13. How does God say He will help you handle temptions to sin?

Life's challenges approach without warning, requiring quick decisions. It's important that you're prepared to respond. Although you can't plan every decision, you can anticipate challenges and have a prepared response. For example, when people ask you to go places or do things you know would be displeasing to God, it's wise to have decided ahead of time what you will say.

If you wait to make a rush decision, you're likely to blow it.

Live, from Vietnam

This week's episode picks up with the mission team still at the Bible college, where they meet with the pastor/director. His passport has been confiscated and at one point he was imprisoned in a three-foot-square isolation cell without a roof, exposing him to the outdoor elements. Because the authorities are watching the school, he lives in a cramped, concealed office. When D.J. asked why he didn't retaliate, the pastor explained that it wasn't about resisting or fighting back, but about carrying on God's work. Team members said that the pastor's humble response broke D.J. and caused something to happen in his spirit. As tears ran down his face, they could tell that something had changed. He was beginning to understand.

Bible college hiding place

"When you're being attacked or persecuted, what keeps you from lashing back or defending yourself?"

—Daniel (D.J.), Bartlesville, OK

"You just take the punishment and go on... It's not like protecting myself or fighting back... but showing God's love."

—College Pastor

Daniel in tears

Do you think it would be easier or harder to live for Christ after enduring opposition and punishment like the director had? Explain.

Watch this week's session on www.undergroundreality.com

FRONTLINE DIARIES

The Holy Spirit Was There

I just got back from a church in the city... The building right across...is a government building, and they have cameras watching this place all the time, and all the phone lines are tapped... It was amazing... One of the pastors from the underground church prayed with me... We talked about all kinds of things...the Holy Spirt was there... What I felt then and there with him in his office was an amazing thing.

We prayed together, and I believe that I have found my calling...to take part in missionary work... it's not about me—it's about doing a great work for God... I am so scared. I would really like some prayer for that. I am going on a twenty-four-hour bus ride to the highlands to distribute five hundred tribal Bibles... There is a bit of danger in this one. I like that. This is where the cowboy rides away.

Love, Daniel

Read more blogs at www.undergroundreality.com
Look for the Underground Reality Blogs and Reality Blog Archives. Plus you'll find ways to pray for persecuted Christians in Vietnam and around the world.

Persecution Around the World

India has a staggering racial, ethnic, religious, and linguistic diversity. The predominant religion is Hinduism, which accepts literally millions of gods. However, in recent years several of India's states have faced religious violence, as radical Hindus have become increasingly hostile toward Christians. In the last five years, there have been reports of pastors and priests beaten and nuns harassed and raped. In 2006 more than two hundred acts of violence were reported against Christians. Several pastors and evangelists were brutally mutilated and killed. Laws in at least five states impose prison terms and hefty fines against anyone who attempts to convert an Indian. Christian humanitarian workers have found that even their efforts to help the sick and needy can be deemed coercion to accept Christ.

Read the latest news from the persecuted church at www.persecution.com.

You'll also find country information, news releases, video clips, and ways you can directly bless persecuted Christians.

Real-Time Response

Do you think you would struggle with hatred toward your persecutors if subjected to resistance and punishment like that inflicted on the underground church? Why or why not?

What bold steps have you taken in recent weeks to identify with Jesus and make a positive impression for Him? What has happened as a result?

Describe how you have grown in your faith and trust in God over the past few weeks.

Being a Christian can be hard. Life isn't always fair. Bad things happen to good people—people like those we've watched in the video—who love God and are doing their best to serve His purposes. But these faithful believers seem to have decided how to respond when faced with trouble and persecution. They've chosen to rely on the Holy Spirit, to be patient and joyful, to love their enemies, to pray for those who persecute them, and to not repay evil with evil. They do this because they realize that God cares deeply for them and promises to never leave them. Knowing this helps them face even the most difficult challenges with joy.

In Perspective

List four tough or tempting situations that you know will come up at home, school, work, church, etc., in the days ahead. These could involve difficult tasks, pressures from people, challenges to your faith, invitations to activities, etc. Along with each situation, describe how you plan to handle the situation in a God-honoring way. (Keep in mind that this may mean avoiding a temptation in the first place.)

1

2

3

4

Spies and Discrimination

Since 1979, Iran's Shiite Muslim government has been set on crushing all other faiths. Mission organizations aren't allowed into the country. Open witnessing to Muslims is banned, and the government sends spies to monitor Christian groups, which endure discrimination in education, employment, and property rights.

Blandina and the bull

Bold Believers

The city of Lyons was ablaze with hatred toward Christians in the year A.D. 177. During a mob attack, a young servant named Blandina was captured and tortured in order to reveal the identity of several Christians. When she refused to disclose the names of fellow believers, the attackers burned her skin with hot irons. But Blandina stood firm, even in the face of persistent torture. One letter from early church historians read, "Blandina was filled with such power that those who kept torturing her in every way, from dawn until evening, were worn out and exhausted." When her abusers saw they couldn't break her, they sent her to prison. There she encouraged other believers on death row. When her time to be executed arrived, Blandina was tied to a post in the arena and wild beasts were set loose to attack her. But none of the animals would approach her, so Blandina was returned to the cell. The next time she was brought out to be executed, her captors placed her on a hot iron grill, then wrapped her in a net and threw her as bait to a raging bull. The beast tossed her around and eventually gored her to death.

Considering the stories of brave martyrs and Christians around the world, you may not feel that you could endure such opposition and hold on to your faith. But if you are faithful to develop your relationship with Jesus and follow His guidance, He will give you the wisdom and strength to stand firm. It's not a matter of feeling strong enough. What matters is that you keep your faith in Christ, relying completely on Him knowing He will give you the strength you need—when you need it.

Today, I Pray

Write a simple prayer, thanking God for His constant love and presence and asking for His help in responding to evil with good.

The Persecuted Church

In Laos, a predominantly Buddhist country, churches are considered subversive and are closely monitored by the government. House church meetings are frequently raided and Christians arrested. Communist leaders in some districts have implemented a program called New Mechanism, in which anyone who doesn't convert to Buddhism or animism is forcibly removed from their district. Christian villagers have been forced to sign documents renouncing their faith. If they refuse, they are forced to leave their homes, and their property is seized or destroyed.

The Word Thru-the-Week

READ: Hebrews 13:5–6

THINK: What is possible with God on your side?

PRAY: Express gratitude to God for His constant help and presence.

READ: 1 Peter 3:8–9

THINK: What are the keys to enduring faith and godly influence?

PRAY: Ask God to give you supernatural love for fellow Christians and for those who persecute you.

READ: Luke 18:1–6

THINK: What do you do when you feel like giving up? Is prayer your first course of action? Are your prayers persistent?

PRAY: Ask God to help you become more persistent in prayer.

READ: Acts 7:57–60 and Luke 23:34

THINK: How do you typically feel toward those who oppose you because of your faith? Is it easier to get angry or to feel compassion?

PRAY: Pray that rather than being fearful or angry, you'll be compassionate toward your persecutors who are deceived by Satan.

READ: Galatians 5:22–23

THINK: Are these traits becoming increasingly evident in your life?

PRAY: Ask God to help your life exhibit the fruit of the Spirit.

READ: Luke 4:1–15; Proverbs 16:6; James 4:7–8

THINK: Are you doing your part to avoid temptation, and to rely on God for strength?

PRAY: Ask God to help you to make wise and bold decisions in the face of difficulty and temptation. Pray God will raise up a mature Christian friend or adult who can help hold you accountable.

Remember to go to www.undergroundreality.com and www.persecution.com this week. You will find ways to pray daily for persecuted Christians around the world.

I Dare You

This week's mission, should you choose to accept it: Refer to your responses in the "In Perspective" section from Session 1. Note the issues, situations, and challenges that you're likely to encounter in the days ahead. These may involve choices regarding activities or entertainment, difficulties with other people, or responsibilities at home, school, or church. They may also be difficult situations you're already facing or about to face. Determine ahead of time how you'll respond in these situations. Set high, godly standards of action, behavior, and character that you'll follow, regardless of the difficulty you encounter or the pressure to make unwise decisions.

Session #7

Heroes of the Faith

"Faith begins where man's power ends."
—George Muller (1805–1898)

WHAT's the Point?

Becoming a hero in God's eyes requires patient endurance and an eternal perspective through perilous times.

WHY Does It Matter?

Real faith is proven through tough times and holds up through persecution, enduring to the end.

HOW Can I Live It?

View persecution as an opportunity to honor God, grow in faith, and look forward to eternity with Christ.

What is it costing you to follow Christ and to fulfill His purposes?

Bible Basis

And what more shall I say? I do not have time to tell about Gideon, Barak, Samson, Jephthah, David, Samuel and the prophets, who through faith conquered kingdoms, administered justice, and gained what was promised; who shut the mouths of lions, quenched the fury of the flames, and escaped the edge of the sword; whose weakness was turned to strength; and who became powerful in battle and routed foreign armies. Women received back their dead, raised to life again. Others were tortured and refused to be released, so that they might gain a better resurrection. Some faced jeers and flogging, while still others were chained and put in prison. They were stoned; they were sawed in two; they were put to death by the sword. They went about in sheepskins and goatskins, destitute, persecuted and mistreated—the world was not worthy of them. They wandered in deserts and mountains, and in caves and holes in the ground (Hebrews 11:32–38).

The Challenge

Considering the plight of Christians in the persecuted church, it's natural to admire their courageous faith. You may even wonder if there's a secret to such great faith. Do those who endure extreme persecution—even to the point of death—know something we don't? Do they have supernatural stamina or insights that elude average believers?

Hebrews 11 highlights heroes of faith—men and women who endured extreme hardship and accomplished great things for God. (Use your Bible's cross references to locate Old Testament accounts of these individuals.) As you consider their stories, note how average these individuals were. Most weren't successful or popular by worldly standards. While their faith was extraordinary, keep in mind that we see their heroism from the other side of history. But from their perspective, they had no guarantee of the outcomes we now read about. Though they trusted God to see them through, not all were rescued from peril. Some made the ultimate sacrifice. What sets these heroes apart was their hope and confidence that life is much more than our time on earth.

Read the second part of Hebrews 11:34: "whose weakness was turned into strength." These words are describing the spiritual heroes of Hebrews 11. Like anyone else, these heroes had weaknesses. **What weaknesses do you feel you have? How do you think God might use your weaknesses?**

Each of us is called to be a hero in God's kingdom, though we fight different battles and face different giants. Many of these are mental and emotional, requiring heroic thinking and proper perspective. Read 2 Corinthians 10:3–6. **Why is the way you think critical to spiritual victory? How would you describe, in practical terms, the strategy this passage gives for godly thinking?**

Most people think a hero is smarter, or stronger, or better than other people, but that's not the kind of hero God looks for. **Read 1 Corinthians 1:26–31. What kind of person does the world consider to be a hero? In contrast, what kind of person does God choose to be a hero?**

What does that tell you about how the world treats Christians?

Witnessing Murder

In Nigeria, Muslims stoned and clubbed a woman to death because she handed out tracts and shared Christ with young Muslims in the village of Izom. In the city of Dutse, seventy homes, businesses, and churches were destroyed and two thousand Christians left homeless. Police said that Muslims rioted over a Christian businesswoman's comments about the prophet Muhammad.

Read Romans 12:1–2. What three things does this passage say will empower you to be a hero and do God's will? What does it mean to be a living sacrifice and stop conforming to the world's pattern?

Wes sobbing

Live, from Vietnam

This week our friends in Vietnam split into two groups. The first group stayed in Saigon to interview some Vietnamese Christians, including Esther, a Hmong teenager whose father is in prison. The second group headed to the Central Highlands to visit the Jaria tribe. Team leaders describe this venture as the most dangerous day of the trip because the government doesn't allow Westerners to associate with the Central Highlands tribal groups. Part of this mission is to deliver five hundred Bibles to an underground church. To get there, they travel sixteen hours one way in a van, passing five government checkpoints. They arrive under the cover of darkness, and must move quickly and silently to enter the worship service in progress.

"[We've been] talking to people that have been in that situation of being beaten and thrown in jail and being told, 'Deny Him, and we'll let you go, or we're going to continue to torture you.' I understand now more of what's on the line... I do the right things, but I'm not living it. And these people are living it 24/7."

—Wes, Tampa, FL

Entering the highlands churc at night

What changes could you make in your life—spiritually or otherwise—that would give you more confidence to attempt something great for God?

Watch this week's session on www.undergroundreality.com

FRONTLINE DIARIES

Missing My Dad

Today has been the most emotional day yet. . .but I have cherished and learned from every minute. When I was listening to this girl tell her story about how her dad went to prison and is still there to this day, it just hit me all of a sudden—this girl never gets to see her dad. . .never gets to curl up on his lap and cry or hear an encouraging word. . .never gets to hear him sing crazy songs. . . never gets to watch him get uncomfortable when she talks about boys or other girl stuff. . .all the things I take for granted. . .I sat there. . .and just bawled and bawled. I told them I couldn't imagine not getting to do all those things with my dad—and to know that he was suffering—it would destroy me. My heart just broke for her. . .and it's been a hard feeling to shake all day...

If somebody took away my dad I would be so lost. And she can sit here and tell us how she encourages her siblings to keep going. . .I would need someone to pick me up. . Just for the record—I love you, Dad, and I don't know what I would do without you. I wasn't with you on Father's Day, but she gets to see her dad for five minutes about every two years. I can't wait to get home and give you a hug. . .

In Him, Bethany

Read more blogs at
www.undergroundreality.com
Look for the Underground Reality Blogs and Reality Blog Archives. Plus you'll find ways to pray for persecuted Christians in Vietnam and around the world.

Persecution Around the World

Colombia is considered one of the most violent countries in the world, plagued by a Marxist government that tolerates guerrilla groups known for extortion, kidnapping, and assassinations. Such groups demand money from churches, threaten missionaries, and force Christian schools and churches to close. Violent acts are funded by drug trafficking. Despite the intimidation, evangelistic efforts have been effective, and the church is growing. However, this has made pastors a target for violence. Ongoing death threats against ministers and their families have forced many into hiding.

Read the latest news from the persecuted church at www.persecution.com.

You'll also find country information, news releases, video clips, and ways you can directly bless persecuted Christians.

Real-Time Response

Who do you admire or consider to be a personal hero? Why? What have you learned from this person?

What are a couple of ways you could be a great example to someone else?

the Salt and Light

Wes broke down at the beginning of the video episode, wrestling with the challenge of whether he would deny Christ if faced with imprisonment, torture, or death for his faith. "The way they teach you in church," he said, "they never say that someone's gonna come and put a gun to your head. We hear it, but we never see it, so we can't grasp it...I'm ashamed to say it, but, yeah, I probably would [deny Christ]." **How do you think you would respond if faced with this same question? Why?**

Growth through Persecution

Nepal's constitution guarantees individuals the freedom to practice their own religion. However, attempts to convert anyone to a different faith carries a three-year jail sentence. The vast majority of people are Hindus, and aggression against Christians is on the rise. Militant Hindus aim to drive out all Christians from the country. Despite all this, the church has grown. Some estimate that there are five hundred thousand Christians in three thousand congregations.

What tactics does the enemy use to keep Christians in free, Western countries from doing heroic things for God?

How can you overcome these tactics and ensure that you accomplish God's ultimate purposes for your life?

Had you thought about the fact that God calls you to something beyond the norm—something heroic? Why or why not, and what could it be?

In Perspective

Describe three aspects, issues, or inabilities in your life that you or others might perceive as weaknesses.

Briefly describe four things you could attempt for God that would be impossible without His help. Try to link at least two of these to a perceived weakness. (You'll revisit this issue in the I Dare You section.)

Bold Believers

At the time of his arrest, one-hundred-year-old Polycarp was the last living associate of Jesus' original twelve apostles. Having had a vision that he would die a martyr, Polycarp wasn't surprised when a group of persecutors came to his home to apprehend him. Rather than fight or flee, he invited them in. Polycarp was such a witness of God's love that his persecutors begged him to deny Christ so they wouldn't have to kill him. But Polycarp wouldn't deny his Lord. So he was brought before the Roman proconsul, who charged him, "Curse Christ, and I will release you!" But Polycarp replied, "Eighty-six years have I served Him, and He has done me no wrong; how can I blaspheme my King who saved me?" Polycarp didn't flinch at the threat of being thrown to wild beasts, then burned alive. When the angry crowd demanded his execution, Polycarp prayed, "Father, I thank You that You have called me this day and hour and have counted me worthy to receive my place among the number of the holy martyrs." As his executioners prepared to nail him to the stake, he asked that they leave him unsecured because God would grant the strength to endure the flames. They granted his request and set a fire around him, but were astounded when the flames didn't appear to consume him. Then they drove a dagger into Polycarp's body, and so much blood flowed that it quenched the fire before he died a martyr in A.D. 161.

Great faith is not a matter of age, experience, circumstances, or relationships. It's about determining to honor God in all situations and trusting that He will take you up on that commitment. It means taking bold steps and trusting God to guide and provide, regardless of the outcome.

Today, I Pray

Write a simple prayer, asking God to help you develop and demonstrate heroic faith.

The Word Thru-the-Week

READ: Hebrews 11:1–12:3

THINK: What is possible for those who trust God completely?

PRAY:: Ask God to lead you into situations where you must trust Him for the extraordinary.

READ: 2 Corinthians 12:9–10

THINK: Do you see your weaknesses, difficulties, and hardships as opportunities to rely on God and grow in His strength?

PRAY: Ask God to help you never to overestimate your own ability and never underestimate His.

READ: 1 Samuel 17:1–51

THINK: What can you learn from David's view of God and of the giant?

PRAY: Ask God to help you make His reputation and honor a far higher priority than your own.

READ: Philippians 1:6

THINK: Are you allowing God to finish what He started in you? Can people see God's peace in you—particularly in difficult times?

PRAY: Make your requests known to God with thanks, and accept His peace.

READ: Ephesians 1:17–19 and Ephesians 2:10

THINK: How courageous are you in pursuing and fulfilling God's purposes? Do you believe God has called you to live a life that glorifies Him and has created you to do good things?

PRAY: Ask God to increase your spiritual intensity.

READ: Ephesians 4:20–24

THINK: Are you surrendering to God and worshiping Him with your entire being? Are you fitting into the world's pattern or God's?

PRAY: Ask God to continually renew your mind so that your thinking is patterned after His Word.

Remember to go to www.undergroundreality.com and www.persecution.com this week. You will find ways to pray daily for persecuted Christians around the world.

I Dare You

This week's mission, should you choose to accept it: With God's help, you will attempt to do something big enough that it wouldn't be possible without God's help and strength. Consider your responses in the "In Perspective" section in Session 1. Choose one of the heroic ideas to accomplish or pursue this week. You may not complete the action this week; perhaps you'll simply begin a new challenge. This could involve starting a campus Bible club, organizing a community outreach, or doing something you've been afraid to do, like giving a speech on a spiritual issue or singing in a youth service.

Don't let perceived weaknesses hold you back. Choose something that may not be considered your strength. That way, God will get the glory.

The Persecuted Church

Saudi Arabia is an Islamic state whose oil wealth is used to finance the spread of Islam around the world. Christians who do mission work or attempt to convert Muslims face jail, expulsion, or execution. Even foreign Christians visiting Saudi Arabia are not allowed to meet for worship.

Session #8

Tears of Joy

"Joy is not the absence of suffering. It is the presence of God."

— Elisabeth Elliot (1926–)

WHAT's the Point?

Joy in the face of extreme opposition can be a most effective witness for Christ.

WHY Does It Matter?

God's love motivates and strengthens us to endure persecution and influence others to trust Jesus.

HOW Can I Live It?

Allow the joy of your relationship with Jesus to provide strength and inspiration to others through difficulty.

Do you have obvious and inspiring joy?

Bible Basis

"As the Father has loved me, so have I loved you. Now remain in my love. If you obey my commands, you will remain in my love, just as I have obeyed my Father's commands and remain in his love. I have told you this so that my joy may be in you and that your joy may be complete. My command is this: Love each other as I have loved you. Greater love has no one than this, that he lay down his life for his friends. You are my friends if you do what I command. I no longer call you servants, because a servant does not know his master's business. Instead, I have called you friends, for everything that I learned from my Father I have made known to you. You did not choose me, but I chose you and appointed you to go and bear fruit—fruit that will last. Then the Father will give you whatever you ask in my name. This is my command: Love each other" (John 15:9–17).

The Challenge

"It was a room of unbelievably, indescribably joyful people…I was just overwhelmed; I didn't know how to feel." That was the reaction of Brad, from Sydney, Australia, when he first entered the secret worship service among the tribal people of Vietnam's Central Highlands. Though the students had already been inspired by their encounters with other courageous individuals in the persecuted church, nothing had prepared them for the explosion of pure joy, love, and gratitude expressed by hundreds of people who risked everything to worship God. So where does this kind of joy come from? And how can it be so plentiful among people who have so little? Apparently, they grasp something about their relationship with God that all Christians need to learn and live by.

Read John 15:9–17. What are some reasons God has given us through Christ to have ultimate joy?

Read Philippians 4:4–9. As a follower of Jesus, **how or why can you be joyful in all situations? What specific instructions do these verses give for having God's peace in all situations?**

Why is it important for your joy to be evident to others, particularly in tough times? How can joy—or lack of it—affect your witness for Christ?

Read Ephesians 1:3–8 and John 15:16. Through a relationship with Jesus, you've been adopted into God's family and restored to the purpose He's always had for you. **How should being a part of God's family affect the way you view your life, your purpose, and your view of Christians around the world?**

Read Acts 16:22–25. Bryant said this about the Vietnamese Christians in the secret worship service: "When I looked into their eyes, most of the people were crying, just tears of joy, because they were just so happy to see us... They were praising and worshiping like the earth was going to blow up in thirty seconds." **Why do you think they were so excited to see the mission team? Why were they worshiping so intensely?**

According to Revelation 21:1–5, what hope do God's people who presently suffer have for the future?

Regardless of what you endure during your earthly lifetime, if you've entrusted your life to Jesus, all hardship, pain, persecution, and suffering will cease forever when you experience the ultimate joy of eternal life in heaven with God!

Underground Growth

Instead of being weakened by persecution, the faith of Vietnamese Christians is growing, and the church is becoming stronger. People are continually turning to Christ in both the registered and unregistered (underground) church, especially among the mountain tribes of Central and Southern Vietnam.

Live, from Vietnam

This week picks up with the mission team split into two groups. Four teens join a secret worship service in the Central Highlands and are met with an indescribable outpouring of love and celebration. Meanwhile, a group of three back in Ho Chi Minh City is torn by the testimony of a girl whose father has been imprisoned for several years, whom she has not seen since 2004. Both groups are emotionally overwhelmed and spiritually challenged by the devotion, stamina, and joy of the Vietnamese Christians. These experiences mark the most intense, life-changing encounters of the entire mission for many of the teens.

How did you feel, or what stood out to you most, as you watched the worship gathering in the Central Highlands?

"I would not be able to handle that... I don't understand that kind of inhumanity... It just makes me nauseous... How in the world do I get there—from this comfortable, complacent American faith to this kind of faith? I definitely think God uses persecution to get people to a closer spot with Him."

—Bethany, Bartlesville, OK

"They were praising the Lord and worshiping, like the earth was about to blow up in thirty seconds."

—Bryant, Tampa, FL

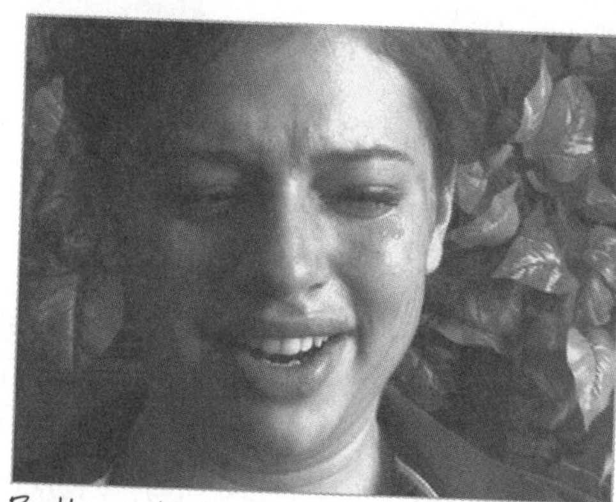

Bethany, broken over Esther's testimony

Watch this week's session on www.undergroundreality.com

FRONTLINE DIARIES

Trip to the Highlands

After twelve hours of driving in a bus, we arrived at the church in the Central Highlands. It was pitch black, and we were instructed to practically run without saying a word straight to the church. As soon as we got off the bus, we could hear the joyous singing and rejoicing of the tribal people. Once we got to the door and removed our shoes we were absolutely mobbed by three hundred people...

These persecuted people were rejoicing with such intensity...Sorry, but I cannot describe in words the way I felt...It was such a spiritual moment for me...it was incredible...We went up and sang two songs for the people; we didn't sound all that great but no one cared. I shared some words of encouragement...and then we were forced to leave two hours prematurely because the police had once again come...

Bryant

Read more blogs at www.undergroundreality.com Look for the Underground Reality Blogs and Reality Blog Archives. Plus you'll find ways to pray for persecuted Christians in Vietnam and around the world.

Persecution Around the World

North Korea is one of the most repressive and isolated regimes in the world, denying every kind of human right to its citizens. Over two-thirds of the people claim no religious affiliation, and Christians comprise less than 2% of the population. In the early 1950s, there were about three hundred thousand Christians in the country. Today, there may be no more than a few thousand. Christians must practice their faith in deep secrecy and are in constant danger. Many North Koreans have fled to China, which is just as repressive toward Christians. Some have been known to return to North Korea to share the gospel. Any North Korean refugees sent back to the country face torture, imprisonment, and often death. Despite the harsh conditions, Christians are quietly adding to their numbers daily.

Read the latest news from the persecuted church at www.persecution.com.

You'll also find country information, news releases, video clips, and ways you can directly bless persecuted Christians.

Real-Time Response

The mission team interviewed a young Hmong Christian girl named Esther, whose father was a tribal youth pastor. Police asked him to meet them one day at a coffee shop—and he's been in prison ever since. That was several years ago. He's confined in a room no larger than a king-sized bed, with eight other men. Conditions are filthy, and the food is almost inedible—such as rice mixed with sand. "I would not be able to handle that," Bethany said. "I don't understand that kind of inhumanity… It just makes me nauseous…How in the world do I get there—from this comfortable, complacent American faith to this kind of faith? I definitely think God uses persecution to get people to a closer spot with Him."

How and why can persecution bring a person closer to God?

During the Central Highlands service, D.J. said that he had never before experienced this type of intensity for the Lord. He went on to say that "it was like God, ten times what I was used to." Brad noted that people in America and Australia don't seem to worship with the same intensity. **Do you agree with this statement? Why do you think this is?**

Real-Time Response, continued

How did the youth team inspire the Vietnamese Christians? How did the Vietnamese Christians inspire the team?

If you could measure your intensity for God at this point in your life, where would you say it is, and why?

What do you think it would take for your intensity to grow stronger?

In Perspective

Joy is a "byproduct" of love—particularly God's love. List specific ways you've experienced God's love.

Joy and gratitude go together. Thankful people are joyful, and joyful people are thankful. What are some things for which you are most thankful?

In what practical ways could you let your joy be more apparent to others?

Bold Believers

Romanus encouraged his fellow Christians, who were being driven out of Antioch, to be brave and to continue serving Christ. After they succeeded in keeping the soldiers out of their church, the emperor ordered that Romanus be seized and whipped. But instead of groaning and screaming, Romanus sang psalms. Because Romanus was singing, the soldiers lanced his sides, his face, and his mouth. Romanus responded by thanking the emperor for giving him more mouths with which to praise Christ. The emperor then had a child of a fellow Christian tortured in front of Romanus, but the child and his mother praised Christ as well. Finally, the emperor ordered the boy to be beheaded and Romanus to be burned at the stake. But before the flames could burn him, a storm quenched the fire. The emperor, disgusted, had Romanus strangled.

The greatest motivators for enduring extreme hardship and standing boldly for God are love and joy. You can't completely control your circumstances, nor can you determine the attitudes and actions of others.

You can, however, rest assured of God's love for you. And regardless of circumstances, it's your choice whether to receive and reciprocate that love and to live in the joy of a relationship with Jesus. By living in God's love and joy, you will ultimately prevail, regardless of what happens in this life.

Today, I Pray

Write a simple prayer, expressing thanks to God for His love and asking for His help in expressing supernatural love and joy toward others.

Persecution in Paradise

Sri Lanka is a potential island paradise, but since the early 1980s violence has reigned. Buddhism is the state religion and is protected and promoted. Though freedom of religion is assured, minority faiths endure discrimination in the areas of taxation, employment, and education. Since 2003, nearly two hundred acts of violence have been recorded against Christians. Buddhist clerics and politicians have now revived efforts to enact a federal anti-conversion law, calling for prison sentences of up to five years and fines for anyone found guilty of converting others. Still, the Sri Lankan church is growing so rapidly that its resources are inadequate to cover evangelism and church planting needs.

The Word Thru-the-Week

READ: 1 John 1:1–7

THINK: Is God's love and friendship to you affecting your love and friendship with others?

PRAY: Give God thanks for His love, friendship, privileges, and purpose.

READ: 1 Thessalonians 1:1–6

THINK: Do circumstances determine your mood, or does your relationship with Jesus maintain your joy? How apparent is your joy?

PRAY: Ask God to help you keep your mind on the right things.

READ: Luke 7:36–48

THINK: How did this woman shed so many tears and express her gratitude so extravagantly? Hasn't Jesus done the same for you?

PRAY: Give Jesus thanks for His forgiveness and joy.

READ: Matthew 10:1 and John 10:10

THINK: How should your God-given position, privileges, and authority as a follower of Jesus affect you attitudes and actions?

PRAY: Give God thanks for making you part of His family, and ask Him to help you treat fellow believers as beloved family members.

READ: Nehemiah 8:10; Matthew 22:36–39; Zephaniah 3:17

THINK: How does God's joy strengthen you? What does this joy say to others who witness it in our lives?

PRAY: Ask Jesus to help you put others ahead of yourself.

READ: Psalm 126:5 and Philippians 3:17–21

THINK: Is your hope of eternity with Christ inspiring you to pursue His purposes with greater passion right now?

PRAY: Pray that you'll endure earthly trials in light of heavenly reward.

Remember to go to www.undergroundreality.com and www.persecution.com for direction and inspiration regarding how to pray daily for persecuted Christians around the world.

I Dare You

This week's mission, should you choose to accept it: Taani said that "it's really important for them [the Vietnamese Christians] to know that there are people out there praying for them and that they're not alone." This week you will purpose to be an answer to prayer for another person—perhaps someone who doesn't even know to pray. Do this by meeting a practical need for that person.

The need may be for a tangible item, financial help, or a service of some kind. It should be something that the person has not been able to do or provide for himself. This may involve giving a significant amount of time, effort, or resource.

Consider doing this anonymously, unless it would provide a better witness to let the individual know that your aim is to honor God.

Session #9

What's Your Battle Cry?

"This generation of Christians is responsible for this generation of souls on the earth."

—Keith Green (1954–1982)

Do you have a cause worth living for—and dying for?

WHAT's the Point?

To know Jesus and spread His message are causes worth giving our lives for.

WHY Does It Matter?

You must be completely surrendered to Christ and fully dependent on God's power if your faith is to endure extreme persecution.

HOW Can I Live It?

Know God's Word, rely on the Holy Spirit, follow God's battle plan, and pray for people in order to see spiritual victory in their lives and yours.

Bible Basis

Finally, be strong in the Lord and in his mighty power. Put on the full armor of God so that you can take your stand against the devil's schemes. For our struggle is not against flesh and blood, but against the rulers, against the authorities, against the powers of this dark world and against the spiritual forces of evil in the heavenly realms. Therefore put on the full armor of God, so that when the day of evil comes, you may be able to stand your ground, and after you have done everything, to stand. Stand firm then, with the belt of truth buckled around your waist, with the breastplate of righteousness in place, and with your feet fitted with the readiness that comes from the gospel of peace. In addition to all this, take up the shield of faith, with which you can extinguish all the flaming arrows of the evil one. Take the helmet of salvation and the sword of the Spirit, which is the word of God. And pray in the Spirit on all occasions with all kinds of prayers and requests. With this in mind, be alert and always keep on praying for all the saints (Ephesians 6:10–18).

The Challenge

What comes to mind when you hear the term "battle cry"? You might relate it to a cause—something worth standing for, fighting for, or even giving your life for. In search of significance, people delve into social and environmental causes, their work, even radical religious efforts. Some causes have merit; others are destructive. But if anyone has a worthwhile cause, followers of Christ do. They've found the ultimate reason for living. It's not about religion; it's about a personal relationship with the Creator, who gave everything to restore our purpose. True success and ultimate victory mean being on God's side and following His directions.

Consider Israel's conquest of Jericho (Joshua 6:1–20). For six days the army marched around the city in silence. On the seventh day, they circled seven times, culminating with a victorious battle cry! At that moment, the massive walls crumbled and the army took the city for God. You too are called by God to engage in a battle—to take back territory from the enemy of our souls, to claim lives for God, and to advance His purposes on earth. That's a cause worth giving your life for.

When Christ's passion and power shows through your life, others will be inspired to trust Him. As the persecuted Christians did in Vietnam, boldly identify with Jesus. **Read Romans 1:16. Why might some people be ashamed to identify with Jesus' message? Are you ashamed, and, if so, why?**

Prayer is not just a weapon; it's how you fight the battle. If you neglect prayer, you have surrendered.

Though God calls you to be bold and strong, you cannot do this on your own. You must rely on the Lord's strength and follow His battle plan. Consider this week's key passage: Ephesians 6:10–18. **Why do you need to put on the armor of God?**

Read Ephesians 6:18 again. What kind of prayer is described? How often are we to pray?

Read Acts 4:29–30. How did the early church respond to persecution?

Jesus has commissioned His followers to represent Him by delivering His good news and bringing freedom to those in spiritual captivity. If Christianity seems uneventful for some, it's because they aren't fulfilling their God-given mission. Many believers go through the same routines over and over, unwilling to step out of their comfort zones by sharing the gospel or getting to know someone who needs a friend. It's no wonder they're bored. God calls you to an adventurous life, requiring trust and courage. **What's something bold or adventurous you'd like to do for God? Describe it in detail.**

The Full Armor of God

- **Belt of truth**—God's Word holds all the armor together.
- **Breastplate of righteousness**—Godly character, integrity, and right relationships with God and people guard your heart.
- **Feet fitted with readiness**—Sure footing allows you to pursue God's purpose and advance the gospel.
- **Shield of faith**—Trust in God allows you to deflect Satan's attacks and honor Christ along with other believers.
- **Helmet of salvation**—Confidence in your salvation guards your mind and allows you to be strong in your thinking.
- **Sword of the Spirit**—Because it is the primary offensive weapon, you must know God's Word and be confident in its power and handle it accurately.

Live, from Vietnam

One of the main reasons the mission team went to Vietnam was to smuggle Bibles to Christians in the underground church. This is the week we see that adventure unfold as the trip culminates in a secret Bible drop. Several team members carrying literature-laden backpacks travel by motorbike to a zoo in the heart of Saigon. There they are approached discreetly by individuals who greet them with the code words: "God bless you." The teens then hand off the backpacks—their mission complete. Wes, from Florida, said, "Once I handed them off, it was as if a big weight lifted off me…It was an adrenaline rush, but exhilarating at the same time…It was like, 'I can't believe I just did that!'"

"Being around all these people and hearing their stories—it totally becomes a part of you…there's no way I could go back to America and just go back to how it was before."

—Bethany, Bartlesville, OK

motorbikes heading to the zoo

saying good-byes

How has your view of persecution and the Christian church around the world changed over the last few weeks?

Watch this week's session on www.undergroundreality.com

FRONTLINE DIARIES

The Drop-Off

Our last activity for the trip may be one of the most exciting: we are dropping off our Hmong tribal Bibles. The plan is to travel on motorbikes to the zoo and meet up secretly with underground Christians—with a code word and everything. Everyone is really excited about doing this one, but not all of us get to do it. Beth and I volunteered to stay behind and buy the backpacks...and then pack the packs. We also may do some scouting at the zoo just to make sure that the entire operation goes down smoothly. This is so exciting... It's a shame that we can't all do it...It's going to be such an amazing experience of reality for those involved. It really feels like a movie... It is really undercover reality (or should that be underground reality?).

Brad

Read more blogs at www.undergroundreality.com
Look for the Underground Reality Blogs and Reality Blog Archives. Plus you'll find ways to pray for persecuted Christians in Vietnam and around the world.

Persecution Around the World

Turkmenistan was one of the republics in the former Soviet Union and had relative freedom in 1991 after the USSR's collapse. But remnants of the old communist system remain. The government has built palaces and memorials all over the country, while its citizens live in poverty. Constitutionally there is freedom of religion, but in practice this is limited to Sunni Islam and Russian Orthodox Christianity. All other minority faiths are subject to severe repression and harassment. Christian students attending universities have been threatened with expulsion. Pastors have been exiled, beaten, heavily fined, and imprisoned. Congregations have been intimidated and forbidden to meet. Evangelical Christians have suffered the most under what is considered to be one of the harshest systems of state control over religious life. Participation in house churches results in fines, property seizure, and salary deductions.

Read the latest news from the persecuted church at www.persecution.com.

You'll also find country information, news releases, video clips, and ways you can directly bless persecuted Christians.

Turkmenistan

Real-Time Response

Brad said, "We just don't sacrifice our comforts...I want to step out and risk my comfort and my security in my witness of Jesus and the way I live for Him." **How about you? In what ways do you intend to step out of your comfort zone and risk your security for God?**

As Taani noted, "These stories are hard to hear...because a lot of them are so brutal. But I think we need to listen... to hear their stories, because... it's reality." **How can you maintain—and help others gain—a growing awareness and appreciation of the persecuted church around the world?**

Real-Time Response, continued

Wes said, "[We've been] talking to people that have been in that situation of being beaten and thrown in jail and being told, 'Deny Him, and we'll let you go, or we're going to continue to torture you.' I understand now more of what's on the line... I do the right things, but I'm not living it. And these people are living it 24/7." **In what area of life—or in what part of your day or week—do you need to strengthen your devotion to Christ? How?**

When the mission team asked the Vietnamese Christians, "What do you want us to tell people back at home?" most responded, "Will you ask them to pray for us?" As one team member affirmed, "It's really important for them to know...they're not alone."

Take time right now to pray for persecuted Christians in Vietnam and around the world.

Persistent Faith

Since the filming of *Underground Reality: Vietnam*, Pastor Quang's house church has been destroyed again. The underground church in the Central Highlands has been raided multiple times. The persecution of the Christians in Vietnam continues. But the faith of the believers remains steadfast.

In Perspective

In light of what you've seen, heard, and read about the persecuted church and bold Christians throughout history, list ways you intend for your life to be different from now on. Though this may include attitudes, try to focus on specific behaviors, disciplines, and actions.

Pray for God's help in making these changes.

Bold Believers

In A.D. 320 Rome was threatened on three borders and its armies needed bolstering. But many Christians who opposed Roman ideals refused to enlist. So Roman officials decided to purge their armies of Christians so that conscientious objectors wouldn't hinder military efforts. The soldiers of the renowned Twelfth Legion of Rome's imperial army—all of whom were Christians—were informed that the emperor had ordered all soldiers to sacrifice to pagan gods. The men refused. They said, "You can have our armor and even our bodies, but our hearts' allegiance belongs to Jesus Christ." As a result, the soldiers were forced to strip in the middle of a frozen lake. There they huddled throughout the winter night, singing praises to God. To entice soldiers to recant, fires and warm baths were prepared along the shore. Eventually, one soldier gave in, making his way toward the fires. But a guard watching from a distance was overwhelmed by the commitment of the remaining thirty-nine Christians. He rose up, stripped off his clothing, proclaimed himself to be a Christian, and took the defector's place on the ice. Within twenty-four hours, the Christians who weren't already dead were forcibly executed.

Billy Graham said, "Courage is contagious. When a brave man takes a stand, the spines of others are often stiffened." Are you setting an example of faithfulness to God despite difficulty at home, at school, at work, or with friends?

Don't underestimate your influence on others who are looking for something worth living for—and dying for.

Today, I Pray

Write a simple prayer, asking God for the kind of uncommon faith, courage, and devotion you've witnessed over the last several weeks.

Growth through Persecution

Since 1983, millions of people in the Sudan—Africa's largest country—have perished due to civil war and genocide. Over the past two decades, the predominantly Muslim government has allowed Muslim extremists to attempt to eliminate a viable Christian presence through bombings of churches and destruction of hospitals, schools, and villages. Pastors and church leaders have been killed. Men, women, and children have been threatened with death or torture if they refuse to convert to Islam. Yet despite these atrocities, the body of Christ continues to grow in the Sudan. Massive population movements have broken down cultural and language barriers, allowing many to receive the gospel in formerly unreached people groups.

The Word Thru-the-Week

READ: Exodus 15:1–3 and Exodus 6:28–7:7

THINK: Are you relying on your strength or God's? Are you doing things your way or His?

PRAY: Give God thanks for being your strength, and pray for help in following His commands.

READ: Romans 1:16–17 and Mark 8:36–38

THINK: Do you view your faith as a private issue? Do those around you see God's love and power in you?

PRAY: Pray for godly boldness and love that is evident to others.

READ: Reread Ephesians 6:10–18

THINK: Do spiritual opposition and attacks tend to get the best of you? What pieces of spiritual armor have you neglected?

PRAY: Pray for spiritual alertness and for other believers who are suffering.

READ: Acts 4:23–31

THINK: When you meet resistance for your faith, do you pray for your enemies and for even more opportunities to honor Jesus?

PRAY: Ask God to help you live in a way that constantly honors Him. Ask Him to work through you in undeniably powerful ways.

READ: Luke 4:18–19 and Hebrews 4:12–16

THINK: How much do you value and rely on God's Word—in easy and difficult times? Do you follow the Holy Spirit's guidance at all times?

PRAY: Ask God to give you a greater hunger for His Word and a greater sensitivity to His Spirit.

READ: John 16:33 and Matthew 6:28–30

THINK: Are you anxious about anything God wants you to give to Him?

PRAY: Thank Jesus for making you an overcomer in all circumstances.

Remember to go to www.undergroundreality.com and www.persecution.com for direction and inspiration regarding how to pray daily for persecuted Christians around the world.

I Dare You

This week's mission, should you choose to accept it:
It's time to step out in faith like never before.

Think about specific people with whom you have considered sharing Christ but never have. Write down their names and make a decision to put fears and inhibitions aside. Don't let opposition or isolation hold you back any longer. Find ways to start conversations this week. Give sincere compliments and ask questions that express genuine interest and concern. Then rely on the Holy Spirit to give you the right words at the right time that will cause these individuals to consider Christ. Asking if you can pray for them can be a bold and effective step. Aim to talk to at least one of these people about Jesus this week.

The Start of Something Great

Congratulations! You are now a globally aware Christian who is beginning to understand the needs and concerns of believers around the world. As one of the team members explained, you can't go back to your old way of thinking. You are going to see things around you in a different way from now on. Even though this course has ended, you and your youth group have many opportunities to stay involved with persecuted Christians.

Think about this question:
What are some things we can do as a youth group to make a greater impact on our campuses, in our community, and around the world—especially for Christians who are being persecuted?

Tell your youth leader about your ideas.
Also, remember that you can support persecuted Christians by staying informed.

Read their stories.
You can do this by visiting www.undergroundreality.com. Also, go to www.persecution.com and sign up for VOM's free weekly emails and/or a free monthly newsletter. Tell other people about the stories you read. You might even give a speech about the persecuted church in one of your classes at school.

Finally, continue to pray for Christians who have lost their jobs, lost their property, been beaten, thrown in jail, and tortured. Your prayers can support them even when you can't be there physically for them.

Thank you for standing with your brothers and sisters in Christ around the world. You are living out the meaning of 1 Corinthians 12: Now you are the body of Christ, and each one of you is a part of it. If one part suffers, every part suffers with it; if one part is honored, every part rejoices with it (1 Corinthians 12:26–27).